HERBERT
RUDEEN

Uncle Arthur's

BEDTIME STORIES

VOLUME THREE

COLOR PHOTO BY STUDIO D'ART →

Arthur S. Maxwell, author of *Bedtime Stories,* is known to thousands of children as "Uncle Arthur."

BEDTIME STORIES

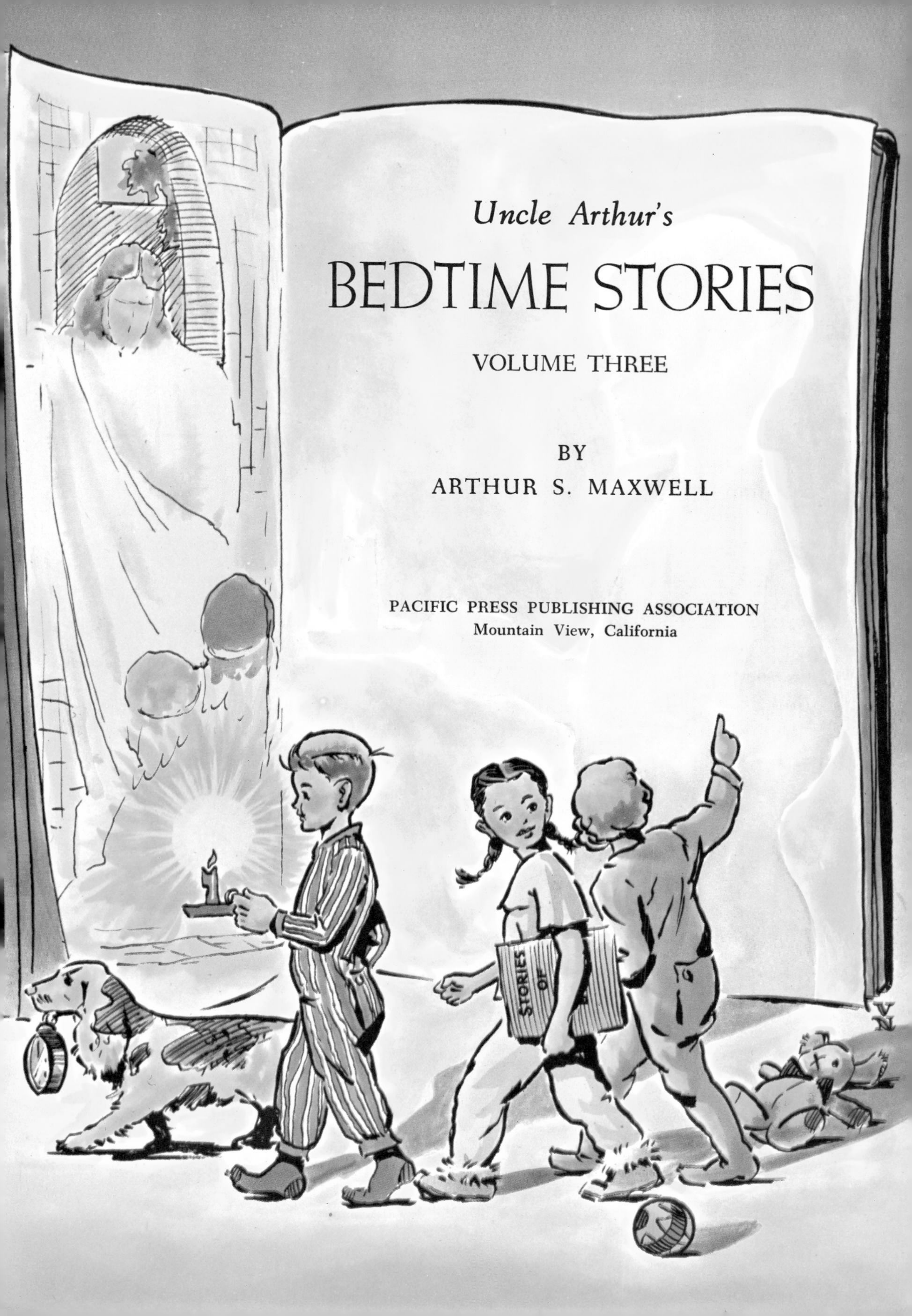
Uncle Arthur's
BEDTIME STORIES
VOLUME THREE
BY
ARTHUR S. MAXWELL
PACIFIC PRESS PUBLISHING ASSOCIATION
Mountain View, California
STORIES OF

This Book is Copyrighted © 1964
by the REVIEW AND HERALD
PUBLISHING ASSOCIATION
WASHINGTON, D.C.
LIBRARY OF CONGRESS CATALOG CARD No. 50-3160
OFFSET IN U.S.A.
Copyright 1928, 1935, 1939, 1942, 1943, 1950, 1956 renewal, 1964 renewal, by the
REVIEW AND HERALD
Publishing Association
COPYRIGHTED IN GREAT BRITAIN
BY THE STANBOROUGH PRESS, LTD.,
WATFORD, ENGLAND

CONTENTS

Lesson Index

Artists participating in the illustration of this volume are Harry Anderson, Robert Berran, Harry Baerg, Siegfried Bohlmann, Kreigh Collins, Thomas Dunbebin, Harvey Fuller, Arlo Greer, John Gourley, Russell Harlan, William Heaslip, Manning de V. Lee, Jeanie McCoy, Don Nelson, Vernon Nye, Lester Quade, Herbert Rudeen, Peter J. Rennings, Elmo White.

VERNON
NYE '49

Tom's Slippers

Tim was not in a very good frame of mind. He was inclined to "grizzle"—if you know what that means. It is sort of halfway between a cry and a grunt. Little boys get the complaint every now and then, usually when they want what they can't get or when they don't like what they do get.

The cause of the grizzling this time was a paintbox. You see, Tim had a paintbox and Tom, his brother, had a paintbox. Unfortunately, Tom had used up all the paints in his box. He liked to pour lots of water into his paints, and then paint big pictures on Daddy's newspapers. So, of course, his paintbox was soon empty.

That being the case, Tom began to cast longing eyes at Tim's paintbox; and Tim, having painted smaller pictures than Tom, and so having a few paint cups left that were not empty, thought it wasn't fair that he should share them with Tom.

Whereupon there was a strong difference of opinion about the matter. Tom made a grab at Tim's paintbox, and Tim sought to defend his box by jabbing Tom in the nose with his

AINTING BY VERNON NYE

ıd in hand, they went off together to hunt for Tim's slippers.

paintbrush. Altogether it was a very unseemly quarrel, and matters might have become very much worse had not Mamma suddenly come on the scene and marched both boys out into the garden to cool off.

But Tim did not forget his troubles, and grizzled all the time about what Tom had done or tried to do. He told Tom that he would never let him have his paints, never.

At last they were called in to supper. And then something else went wrong.

They had to change their garden shoes and put on their slippers when they came into the house, but when they started to do so, poor little Tim discovered that his slippers were missing. He looked high and low, but they were nowhere to be seen.

By this time Tom had his slippers on, which only made Tim more desperate.

"Huh, huh, huh," he began to grizzle again, "I can't find my slippers. Huh, huh, huh!"

Once more he looked in every corner he could think of,

wandering around disconsolately in his socks, crying, "Huh, huh, huh, somebody's got my slippers."

And then a beautiful thing happened.

As poor little Tim came into the dining room again crying, "Huh, huh, huh," Tom took off one of his slippers and said, "Here you are, Tim; we'll have one each."

Tim's face lighted up with a smile as he eagerly seized the slipper and put it on his left foot. Then, hand in hand, they went off together to hunt for Tim's slippers. How funny it was to hear them wandering around the house—clod, thump, clod, thump, clod, thump—each with one foot in a slipper.

Suddenly there was a cry of joy. Tim's slippers had been found! In their usual place, of course, under his bed. With great rejoicing they came downstairs together, hands clasped and faces radiant.

After supper they were allowed to stay up a little while, as Mamma wanted to finish the ironing before putting them to bed.

So they started painting Daddy's newspaper again, and two brushes could be seen dipping vigorously and with perfect peace and harmony into Tim's paintbox.

Tom's happy little thought had driven all the grizzles away.

The Twins' Desire

When I'm old as you, Daddy,
  I shall drive your car
Down the town and back again
  Where the sweetshops are.

When I'm old as you, Daddy,
  I shall stay up late,
Never go to bed at night,
  Till it's half past eight.

When I'm old as you, Daddy,
  I shall buy a boat,
Sail it out upon the sea,
  Get inside and float.

When I'm old as you, Daddy,
  I shall never eat
Cabbages and cauliflowers—
  Just nice things and sweet.

When I'm old as you, Daddy,
  I shall put my feet
High up on the mantelpiece;
  Choose your comfy seat.

When I'm old as you, Daddy,
  Where will you be then?
Will you love me just the same?
  Come and play again?

Uncle Arthur.

The Burglar

Muriel came bounding in from school, bubbling over with excitement.

"Oh, Mamma," she cried, "what do you think? Why, almost all the girls in my class are going to Jenny's party on Thursday night."

"Are they?" said Mamma, trying hard to be interested, though she was feeling very tired. "That will be nice."

"But that's not all," said Muriel; "they've almost all told me that they are going to have the loveliest new dresses—silk and nylon, you know, and pretty things like that."

"They must be happy, then," said Mamma.

"Yes, but, Mamma, what about me? I can't go in my old dress."

"It's not very old," said Mamma. "Why, you had it new for your birthday. Anyhow, dear, I don't think I could possibly make another dress by Thursday."

Muriel did not notice the look of utter weariness that passed over Mamma's face at the very thought of taking on another job just now.

"Mamma!" she cried, "you don't mean to say that I cannot have a new dress for Thursday? Why, I've got to have one! I must! I couldn't go to Jenny's party without it. What would they think of me? All the other girls with new dresses on, and me in that old cotton thing! Of course I must have a new one."

The bright, happy look that was on Muriel's face as she bounded into the dining room faded away, and in its place was an ugly scowl. The more she thought about her fancied grievance, the darker the scowl became. Gradually she worked herself up into a thoroughly bad temper.

"I must have my new dress!" she cried, stamping her foot on the floor.

"Now, come," said Mamma sternly. "It is not becoming for a little girl to behave like this. I don't think you would do it if Jenny were here."

"I wouldn't care who was here," cried Muriel wildly, tears running down her cheeks.

"Now, Muriel," said Mamma, "this is very foolish of you. You must be overtired. Please go to your bedroom. I will bring you your supper later."

Muriel stormed out of the room and up the stairs. Some time later Mamma went up with a very plain supper. She did not say much, only stopping long enough to put little Jimmie —Muriel's little brother—to bed. He did not bother his head about Muriel's troubles, though he thought it was strange that she had had to go to bed so early.

An hour passed. Muriel tried to sleep, but could not. Conscience was keeping her awake. She knew she should be sorry for her very naughty conduct, but something kept her from saying so. She rolled and tossed upon her bed. Another hour passed; then another. At last she dropped into a troubled sleep. It seemed hardly a moment before she was awakened by a small hand tugging at her nose. It was Jimmie.

"Sis, sis," he was saying, "I'm frightened. Let me come into your bed."

Muriel sat up sleepily and rubbed her tired eyes. "What's the matter, Jimmie?" she said, lifting the shivering little chap in beside her.

"Oh, didn't you hear it? The noise—downstairs!"

"No," said Muriel. "I was asleep. What sort of noise was it?"

"Someone walking about," said Jimmie.

Muriel listened. It was a dark night, and very still. A cool breeze came in from the wide-open window.

The clock in the dining room struck—one, two.

"Why, it's two o'clock," said Muriel. "There can't be anybody about now."

"But there was, just a little while ago," said Jimmie. "You should have heard."

Suddenly Muriel's heart stood still, and she seemed to tingle all over. She too had heard a footstep in the room beneath her.

"Did you hear it then?" said Jimmie.

"Yes," said Muriel. "I wonder——"

"Do you think it's a burglar?" asked Jimmie in a whisper.

"It might be," said Muriel, now very much frightened herself.

"What shall we do?" asked Jimmie.

Muriel didn't know what to say. Her first thought was to dive under the bedclothes. Then she remembered how she had once told the girls at school what she would do if burglars ever came to her house. She thought a moment.

"There it is again!" whispered Jimmie, pressing closer to his big sister.

"Jimmie," said Muriel, "do you know, I'd really like to see a burglar, just once, so I could tell the girls at school."

"Would you? I wouldn't," said Jimmie.

"Will you come with me if I go down?" asked Muriel. "I'll look after you."

Jimmy was doubtful, but at last decided to go. Together they slipped out of bed. Ever so quietly they crept to the bedroom door and opened it.

Creak! went the hinges, so loud that the two nearly ran back to bed. But they held each other's hands a little more tightly and went toward the stairs.

Creak! went the top stair.

They held their breath, waited a moment, and then went down a little farther.

Creak! went the fifth stair.

Again they waited. Then on farther.

Creak! went the landing.

"He'll hear us," whispered Jimmie, growing more fearful. "Let's go back."

"Wait a minute," whispered Muriel, pressing his little hand. "We're nearly there. See, there's a light under the dining room door. I must see what a burglar's like, for I may never have the chance again."

"But won't he hurt us?" asked Jimmie.

"We'll run too fast," said Muriel.

They were down in the hall now.

Slowly and ever so quietly they moved toward the door. It was slightly ajar. Muriel pushed it just a teeny-weeny bit. Then a teeny-weeny bit more. And a teeny-weeny bit more. So it was opened, wider and wider, until at last Muriel thought she could put her head round just enough to see inside.

Jimmie held her hand very tightly as she peered round the corner.

"Muriel!" cried a voice, and a pair of scissors clattered on the floor.

"Mamma!" cried Muriel.

They looked at each other.

"Mamma! what are you doing here at this time of night? It's nearly half past two. What is keeping you up?"

"Just a little dressmaking," said Mamma.

"Not my dress, surely," cried Muriel. "Oh, it is, Mamma! I don't deserve it! You shouldn't have stayed up so long! You were so tired."

She threw her arms round Mamma's neck. "I'm so, so sorry," she said, her tears falling fast.

"Never mind," said Mamma. "The dress is nearly done now. Let us all go to bed. But what is Jimmie doing down here?"

"Muriel said I would see a burglar if I came downstairs, and now there isn't one," muttered Jimmie, disappointed.

"I'm sorry," said Muriel, as they went upstairs together, "but Mamma is surely better than a burglar, isn't she?"

"S'pose so," said Jimmie.

And so mother love, forever patient, forever long-suffering and forgiving, triumphed again.

Coals of Fire

"Daddy," cried Donovan, running in from school, "that boy Lionel is the meanest fellow in the school."

"Hello, hello, what's the matter now?" said Daddy.

"Oh, he's just terribly mean. He's always calling me names, and everything I do he says is bad or stupid, and he's always setting the other boys against me with his tales."

"Tut, tut, tut!" said Daddy. "It surely can't be as bad as that."

"Yes, it is," said Donovan. "And what's more, I'm not going to stand it any longer. Big as he is, I'm going to fight him to-morrow."

"Well, that's interesting," said Daddy, smiling. "I hope you will tell me when it's going to come off, so I can come along and pick up the pieces."

"There won't be any pieces left of him," said Donovan angrily.

"What? are you going to swallow him afterward?"

Donovan laughed.

"Do you know," said Daddy, "I can tell you how to pay that boy back."

"Can you?" cried Donovan, all eagerness. "How?"

"Would you like to put some coals of fire on his head?"

"Anything," said Donovan. "Anything."

"Well, I'll get the prescription for you so you can do it."

So Daddy went into his study and brought out a book. After a little searching he found the place.

"Ah, here it is," he said. "Listen, Donovan: 'If thine enemy hunger, feed him; if he thirst, give him drink: for in so doing thou shalt heap coals of fire on his head.' Rom. 12:20."

"Aw," said Donovan, "that's no good; I'd rather fight him."

"But," said Daddy, "this is much better. If you fight him,

you cannot hurt him very much; but this way you pour coals of fire on his head. You will burn all the meanness out of him."

"Fine!" said Donovan. "But I don't like that way of doing it."

"Why not try it?" said Daddy. "It's worth trying, anyway."

"I'll see," said Donovan. "I'll think it over."

Donovan thought it over, and it was not long before something began to happen.

Next morning, on his way to school, whom should he meet but the hated Lionel.

"Just my luck," Lionel said as he came up with Donovan. "Got up late and missed my breakfast. Suppose you've been eating the fat of the land."

"No breakfast!" said Donovan kindly. "You must be starved. Do have my lunch right now. Yes, I did have a good breakfast, and I am not a bit hungry, so you really must have my lunch."

Lionel was as surprised as if he had received a blow between the eyes. He looked first at Donovan and then at the lunch.

"You don't mean it," he said.

"Really I do," said Donovan. "Do take it."

"That's nice of you. Thanks," said Lionel, taking the little parcel and beginning to eat. "But you will have some yourself, won't you?"

Donovan took a sandwich, and they walked on to school together, munching in silence.

"Hot this morning," said Lionel after they had gone some distance. "Wish I could get a drink somewhere."

"A drink?" said Donovan. "Let me see, where can we get one? I should like one too."

"Pity we can't get some lemonade in that store over there," said Lionel.

"I've an idea," said Donovan. "I have two dimes with me. What about it? Let's go over, shall we?"

"Well, I don't want to take your money," said Lionel. "I'll wait till we get to the playground."

"Oh, no, come along with me," said Donovan. "We'll have a glass each. Looks good, doesn't it?"

So they went in, bought a glass of lemonade each, and then hurried on to school.

That evening Daddy was waiting at the gate for Donovan.

"Well," he said, "how did the fight go? I hope you won."

"I did," said Donovan with a twinkle in his eye. "I just burned him all up."

"Whatever do you mean?" asked Daddy.

"Why, I did what you said. I fed him with my lunch, and I gave him a drink of lemonade, and—well, he suddenly changed. He's been as different as could be all day. We've been like old friends all the time."

"Splendid! Well done, Donovan!" said Daddy. "I hope you'll win all your battles just like that."

Pearlie's Pennies

Pearlie was one of those lucky little children who live by the seaside. Her home was only ten minutes' walk from the beach. Almost any time she wished she could walk along the sea front or go and dig in the sand. No waiting for months and months while Daddy saved up enough money to take her there. The sea and the sand were almost at her doorstep. Wasn't she a fortunate little girl!

One would think that, having so many good things, Pearlie would have been the very best little girl in the world. Surely a little girl living so close to the sea could never be naughty! But alas, if the truth must be told, she could—when she felt like it—be the most disobedient child you ever heard of.

Pearlie had a dear, kind Mother, who did all she could to please her and make her happy. If anything, Mother was too good to her, and let her have her own way too much. But Pearlie somehow didn't seem to appreciate it.

One day her uncle came to visit them. While he was there, Pearlie was the nicest child on earth, and "butter wouldn't melt in her mouth," she was so good. Uncle was so pleased with

her that he gave her a silver dollar and ten bright pennies all for herself, and went away thinking that no uncle had a nicer little niece anywhere.

But, what a change when he had gone! Dear me! Mother asked her to lay the supper table.

"Don't want to lay supper," said Pearlie.

"But you must help Mamma sometimes."

"Don't want to help you. You're always asking me to do something I don't want to do."

"But aren't you going to have supper as well as the rest of us?"

"Yes, but I never get any time to myself; you are always making me work."

"Don't be foolish, Pearlie. Lay the table at once."

Thinking she had gone about far enough, Pearlie began to lay the table, but with a sulky face and her lips pouting out almost beyond the end of her nose.

At suppertime there was another scene, over the money Uncle had given her. Mother suggested very nicely that she had better put it in her savings box so that she could buy something special for herself on her next birthday.

"Don't want to put it in my box," snapped Pearlie.

"But what do you want to do with it, then?" asked Mother.

"Buy candy with it. Uncle said I could do what I like with it."

"But Mamma is here to tell you what is best."

"And you always say I have to put it in my box, and I never have any pennies to spend, and—and——"

Pearlie began to pout worse than ever, and sat back in her chair so far that she seemed almost to disappear under the table.

Mother took her upstairs and put her to bed, but it didn't seem to make any difference. All next day she was the same. By dinnertime Mother was so tired of her that she said she had better go for a walk by the sea, and let the wind blow the crossness out of her. Pearlie agreed to this suggestion quickly, thinking it would save her from helping Mother dry the dishes.

"Good-by, dear," said Mother. "And do come back good. You can walk along the front as far as the pier, but don't go on the pier or on the breakwaters."

"All right, Mamma," said Pearlie; "good-by."

Gaily she trotted along the promenade, watching the waves

roll up on the shore, and stopping now and then to talk with other children who were playing on the beach. After a while she reached the pier.

She had often been on the pier with her mother, and enjoyed it very much indeed. She could never understand why she was not allowed to go on it by herself, and as she came up to the entrance this time, the thought came to her, "Why not go on now? Mamma will never know, and I shall have a really nice time all by myself. I wonder how much it is."

She looked about and saw a notice: "Admission 10 cents. Children half price." She felt in her pocket. Hurrah! She had brought all her pennies and the dollar as well. Of course she wouldn't spend that, for she really wanted to buy something nice with it, but the pennies, well—no one would know, so she used five of her pennies to go into the pier arcade.

Once through the gate she felt safer. Mother would never be able to find her now, she thought. She could spend the rest of her pennies as she liked. Soon she saw a chocolate machine and decided that one penny should go in there. She felt very proud of herself as she pulled out the little brown square of chocolate, and how nice it did taste!

Then she saw a weighing machine, and thought it would be nice to feel what it was like to be weighed. She put in her penny and something went wiggly-woggly in front of her and that was all, except that she heard her precious penny drop down somewhere inside. It was rather disappointing.

Then she spied a machine that had a little gun inside. "This looks exciting," she said to herself, pushing her penny into the slot. She pulled the trigger, but nothing happened. She pulled it again and banged the machine with her hand, but to no

avail. Then she noticed a slip of paper inside with the words "Out of Order." Keenly disappointed, she walked on.

Her next penny she tried in a machine that offered to tell her fortune. Out came a tiny slip of paper with a lot of small print on it which she could not understand.

"Horrid old machines!" she said, getting as angry with them as she had been with her mother the night before. "You've taken four of my pennies and I've only one left!"

How she wished she had not been so foolish! But it was no use crying; they were gone. She put her hand in her pocket for the rest of her money, but could not feel it. What could have happened to it? Had she lost it?

Desperately she pulled everything out of her pocket. Out came the chocolate wrapper, a piece of string, a glove, a paper bag, and lastly a handkerchief.

As she pulled out the handkerchief there was a tinkle on

the wooden boards of the pier, and away went her last penny and the dollar in different directions.

The penny did not get very far. Pearlie watched it go into a crack in the boards and fall through into the sea. Then her eyes caught sight of her precious dollar rolling toward the side of the pier, where there was nothing to prevent it from leaping after the penny.

"My dollar, my dollar!" cried Pearlie.

On went the dollar and after it went Pearlie. Nearer and nearer it rolled to the edge, where only a chain, eighteen inches from the floor, stood between the little girl and the water far below.

"I've got it!" she cried, stooping down and stretching out her arm.

But no, it slipped out of her fingers and slid over the edge. Grabbing at it again, Pearlie lost her balance and slipped under the protecting chain. Splash!

When Pearlie woke up she found herself in her own bed at home with a hot-water bottle at her feet and a nice fire blazing in the room. Mother was sitting beside her bed.

Pearlie began to remember things, and put out her hand. Mother took it in hers.

"I'm so sorry, Mamma dear," she whispered. "I'll never, never be so bad again."

Selfish Sandy

Sandy McFarlane had just one big fault. He was the most selfish little boy you could imagine. He always wanted to be first in everything, and if he didn't get the best of everything, he made a terrible fuss about it. And when it came to playing with toys—well, of course, Sandy kept them to himself as much as he could, and quarreled with everybody who played with him.

Birthday time came around. Sandy had let it be known that what he wanted was a clockwork boat and a new railroad engine with rails and cars, a station, signals, and all the rest.

On his birthday morning Sandy found two nicely wrapped packages by his plate at breakfast. Opening them with great glee, he discovered the very things for which he had asked. There wasn't a happier boy in the whole town.

Then he noticed a letter inside one of the parcels.

"Perhaps Daddy has given me some money as well," he said to himself, his eyes sparkling.

Tearing open the envelope, he read the following message:

"My Dear Sandy,

"I hope you will have a very happy birthday. Here are some things that you wanted. I have bought them for myself, but I am lending them to you to play with for a little while. Look after them well, as I may want them back someday.

"With fondest love from

"Daddy."

Sandy couldn't quite see what it all meant. He thought it was a big joke. "Fancy Daddy's saying he bought these for himself! Just as if he would take them to the office with him!"

He soon forgot all about the letter and took the precious toys out into the garden. Filling a tub with water he quickly had the clockwork boat sailing round and round in it. Then he assembled the tracks, and set the engine going. He was enjoying himself immensely when Tony, his baby brother, turned up on the scene.

"Don't touch that boat, Tony," he said.

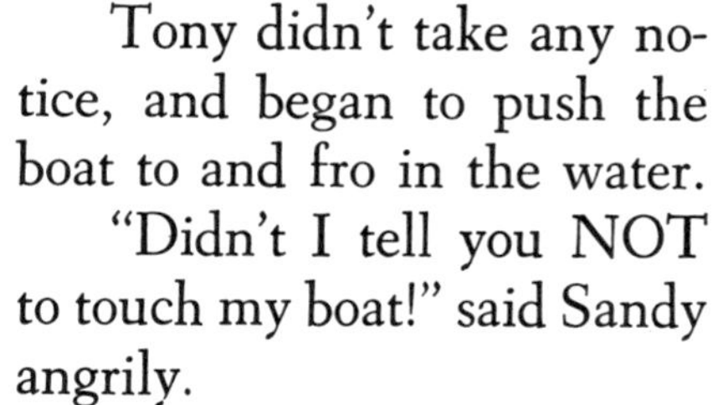

Tony didn't take any notice, and began to push the boat to and fro in the water.

"Didn't I tell you NOT to touch my boat!" said Sandy angrily.

Still Tony didn't take any notice.

Sandy walked over and

slapped his little brother on the face. "There," he said, "now you'll know not to touch my things!"

Poor little Tony ran indoors screaming.

That night, when Daddy returned from his work, he heard all about the affair in the garden.

"So he has started again, has he?" said Daddy. "Well, we will see what we can do. Pack the things up for me, will you, Mamma?"

Next morning Sandy wanted his toys. They were nowhere to be found. He began to get frantic.

"Mamma, where is my boat? I can't find it anywhere. And where's my train?"

"Oh, I should have told you," said Mamma quite calmly. "Daddy thought he would use them today. It's quite all right, dear; he will bring them back."

"He can't have taken them," said Sandy. "What would Daddy do with a train and a boat at his office? I am sure they are here somewhere. Anyway, he wouldn't take my things like that."

"Oh, but you mustn't forget they are *his* things. He bought them for himself. I think he only lent them to you, didn't he?"

Sandy's face fell. Was this, then, the meaning of that letter in the parcel?

All unknown to Sandy the toys were still in the house, packed away carefully in the cupboard under the stairs. But during the day six interesting little invitations had been sent out to six little boys in the neighborhood whom Daddy knew quite well.

The next afternoon, while Mother kept Sandy upstairs busy with some little job, the six boys arrived in the back yard, and under Daddy's supervision, began to enjoy themselves with a railroad train and a clockwork boat. Daddy left them after a while, and what fun they did have together! Shrieks of laughter and yells of delight filled the yard.

"What's that noise outside?" said Sandy.

"Noise?" said Mother. "Sounds like boys playing, doesn't it? I shouldn't bother if I were you."

But Sandy's curiosity had been aroused. Rushing to the window of the back bedroom, he looked out.

"Mamma, look!" he cried. "They are using my engine. Stop it, you children! Leave it alone at once! You wait till I come downstairs!"

With that he left the window and dashed down the stairs three at a time and out into the back yard.

Running to the railroad tracks, he picked up the engine, the cars, and the station, and began running toward the house. On the way he ran into Daddy.

"What are you doing with my engine and cars?" asked Daddy. "You had better put them down at once."

"But these children are playing with them, and they'll break them," said Sandy.

"That doesn't matter at all," said Daddy. "I have invited them to come here, and they are my little guests. I want you to be polite to them."

"But they're my cars and engine," wailed Sandy.

"I beg your pardon," said Daddy, "but you are quite mistaken. I only lent them to you for a little while. If you had not been so mean and selfish over them, you might have kept them always. But they are still mine, and I'm giving them to some children who can play with them happily without quarreling."

And so saying Daddy gave the engine to one boy, the station to another, the cars to a third, the boat to another, and so on until everything had been given away. Then he bade them all good-by, and sent them away rejoicing over their unexpected gifts.

Poor Sandy was heartbroken. He went upstairs to his bedroom and wept for a long time. But the lesson his Daddy taught him that day was never forgotten, and "Selfish Sandy" gradually—after a good long time—became known as "Sandy the Unselfish."

Gladys Greatheart

"What's behind those big brown eyes, Gladys dear?" asked Mamma as she stepped quietly up beside her little daughter.

"I'm thinking," said Gladys.

"You're always thinking," said Mamma.

"Am I?" she said, going off into dreamland again.

Gladys loved to go out in the back yard all by herself and sit on a log or on the lawn and plan beautiful things or count the ants at her feet or lie on her back and watch the clouds go by. Then she would come indoors again, bringing sunshine and happiness everywhere she went. Nothing pleased her more than to gather flowers for the table or run messages for Mamma or have Daddy's slippers ready for him just in the right place when he came home. That's why they called her Gladys Greatheart.

"What's behind the clouds, Mamma?" she asked after a little while.

"The big blue sky," said Mamma.

"And what's behind the big blue sky?"

ARLES CAREY

ys loved to go out in the back yard all by herself and plan beautiful things.

"The stars." Mamma's voice was tender.

"And what's behind the stars, Mamma?"

"More stars," said Mamma.

"And what's behind the more stars?"

"Ah, that's where God lives."

"How far away He must be!"

"It seems a long way to us, but it's not far to Him," said Mamma. "He can travel so swiftly, you see. He could come all the way from His home to ours in less than a second."

"What about the stars in the way?"

"Oh, He knows the way here."

"Do you think He has time to think about us?"

"I'm sure He does. And He loves us very much, and wants us to be good and kind as He is."

"And does He love all the little children in the world?"

"All of them, just the same. You see, we all belong to Him, so we are all just one big family in His sight."

"What a lot of brothers and sisters I must have!"

"Yes," said Mamma, "hundreds and thousands of them. And God wants us to love them all as He does, and

to be kind to them, especially to the poor and sick, and those who cannot care for themselves."

Gladys thought for quite a long time.

"Peggy is sick," she said, breaking the silence. "May I take her my painting book this afternoon? And the brush, of course."

"If you wish," said Mamma. "I am sure Jesus would be pleased."

"Do you think He will know about it?"

"Oh, yes. The angels will tell Him at once, and all heaven will be happier."

"Do you really think so?"

"Oh, yes," said Mamma. "It's just as if you gave it right into His own hand, for did not Jesus say one time long ago, 'Inasmuch as ye have done it unto one of the least of these My brethren, ye have done it unto Me'?"

"I think I will take that nice pincushion you made for me as well, Mamma. I think Peggy would like to play with that too."

So they planned to visit Peggy; and from Peggy they went to others who were sick and poor, scattering joy and gladness along their pathway, and making friends with the children of God, who made the skies and filled them with stars.

And when Jesus comes back through the stars to take His people to their heavenly home, I think He will want to take Gladys Greatheart with Him too, don't you?

Secret of Happiness

The radio weather report said that snow was coming. This was good news for Joe and Gerald. It set them ablaze with energy.

They had often talked about making sleds for themselves, but so far had never done so. The good news about the snow made them decide to make one each, and so they eagerly began the task.

Every moment they could spare from their schoolwork the boys spent in the shed in Gerald's back yard, sawing, planing, hammering, until at last, to their great joy, the sleds were completed and ready for the snow to fall.

But it did not come. Probably the clouds were blown away after the weather experts had looked at them. However that may be, the sad fact is that for many days there were two sleds in the shed, with nothing to slide them on.

School closed for Christmas, and still there was no snow. Day after day went by, cold and wet. There seemed about as much prospect of snow as of a heat wave. The boys gave up hope and wished they had never taken the trouble to make their sleds.

At last Christmas Eve arrived, and with it came a sudden change. The rain stopped, the thermometer went down with a rush, and a strong wind arose.

"Something is going to happen," said Joe, as he went to bed that night. And he was right.

In the morning the clouds had gone, and the rising sun glistened on a vast expanse of snow. A heavy fall had covered the whole landscape with a glorious white mantle.

Gerald was overjoyed. As soon as he awoke he guessed what had happened, for he could see the reflection of the snow on the ceiling. He leaped out of bed, dressed as quickly as he could, and rushed down the garden to the shed where the precious sleds had been stored so long. He hauled them both over the snow up to the house, and then ran off to find Joe.

How happy they were! This was better than their highest expectations. No Christmas Day could have started more joyously for them. They decided that they would go off at once to a neighboring hill and enjoy themselves to the full.

They trotted off down the street, dragging their sleds behind them. School friends shouted to them, all eager to share in the fun.

"Lucky fellows," they cried; "let's have a ride."

"Not now," cried Joe and Gerald, "we're going off by ourselves today."

"Lend us one of your sleds," cried another.

"Nothing doing!" shouted Joe. "You should have made one for yourself."

Ralph Morton, the lame boy, waved his hand cheerfully from his window, and wished them a jolly day.

"Nice of him, wasn't it?" said Gerald.

"Yes," said Joe, " 'specially as he can never hope to pilot a sled of his own."

Just then they passed Madge Green's house. They had always been friendly with her and her little sisters. She greeted them cheerfully as usual, and wished them a happy Christmas.

"Wish I could come for a slide," she said, "but I can't today. I'm helping Mother all I can, so that she may have a really happy Christmas."

The boys passed on. Soon they were out of the town and ascending the hill, dragging their sleds behind them. Then they prepared their slide and the fun began.

Swish! Away they went down the hill. Then up to the top again. Then another glorious slide. So they played together for a couple of hours.

After a while, however, Joe noticed a change coming over Gerald's face.

"What's up, Gerald?" asked Joe with some concern, as

they climbed the hill together, this time a bit more slowly.

"Nothing much," said Gerald, "only somehow I'm not getting as much fun out of this as I thought I would."

"Aren't you?" said Joe. "I'm not, either. Of course, it's nice in a way, yet I don't feel comfortable. I wonder why it is?"

"Funny we should both feel the same way," said Gerald, "isn't it?"

"Very funny," said Joe, as they trudged on up to the top.

Swish! Down they went again.

On the way up next time they talked about their strange feelings again.

"I think I know what's the matter," said Joe.

"What?" asked Gerald.

"I keep thinking about Ralph."

"So do I," said Gerald. "And Madge and the others. I wish we hadn't left them behind. Bit mean of us, wasn't it?"

"Yes," said Joe.

There was silence again as they climbed slowly upward.

"I think we'll have only one more," said Joe.

"All right," said Gerald.

They had the last slide, and then turned toward home. On the way they talked of how they would spend the afternoon. As they reached the town, they began calling at the homes of some of their little friends who had no sleds. What Gerald and Joe said to them seemed to make them very happy.

Dinner was scarcely over when there was a loud knock at their front door. Running out, Joe and Gerald found a happy, excited group of children waiting for them.

"Hurrah!" they all cried when they saw the two boys. "I'll be first," said one, and "Me, me, me, first!" called another.

Then sorting the visitors out, Joe and Gerald put two or three of them on each sled, and began to give them rides up and down the street. Oh, the shrieks of joy! How they all did laugh and yell!

All the afternoon they kept it up—except for a game of snowball now and then—giving rides to all the children in turn, until at last, too weary to run any more, Joe and Gerald sent them all home and put the hard-worked sleds back in the shed once more.

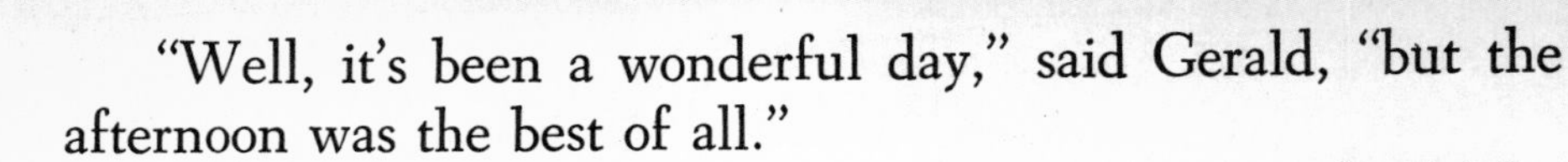

"Well, it's been a wonderful day," said Gerald, "but the afternoon was the best of all."

"It really was," said Joe. "What a great time we had! The morning on the hill wasn't anything like it."

"Do you know, Joe," said Gerald, "I had made up my mind that I never would let anyone else use my sled, but I didn't really begin to enjoy it until I started to share it with the others."

"I think that's why we both felt so much happier after dinner, don't you?" said Joe.

"Sharing things is real fun," Gerald agreed.

He was right. It is the secret of happiness.

PAINTING BY HARRY BAERG

H. BAERG

The Cat That Paid the Bill

This is a true story about two boys and a cat. It happened many years ago in the city of Bath, England. The boys, with their Mother and sister, had come from Wales to attend some gospel services in a big tent in the city.

The family was not well off, and money just then was very scarce. Not being able to afford many holidays, they felt that this trip to Bath was something very wonderful, and they enjoyed every moment.

Then one Thursday morning Mother called the boys to her and told them that she could not afford to stay any longer, and that they must leave the next day.

Bertie and Willie were very much disappointed, and could not understand why they had to leave while all the other people stayed. They did not think it was a bit fair, and they pleaded with Mother to let them stay. But she told them again that there was no money left, and they would have to go home.

"But can't we ask Jesus to send us the money?" said the boys. "He has plenty, and surely He wants us to stay to all these meetings."

"Of course you can ask Him," said Mother; and the next morning—on the very day they were to return home—they knelt down and asked Jesus to send them fifteen shillings—which was quite a lot of money in those days—so they could stay over the weekend.

Then they left their lodgings and went to the big tent. Believing that Jesus would answer their prayer, they did not tell anybody that they might have to leave that day, and they did not say good-by to anyone.

Afternoon came. The children's meeting closed, and the boys started back to their apartment. Still no money had come. It seemed that they would have to return home after all.

Now, in order to reach the house in which they were staying, the boys had to cross right through the town from Beechen Cliffs to Walcot. Usually they followed the lower Walcot road, but this time they turned into the Paragon, a crescent of large houses.

In those days there was a cabstand on the corner of the Paragon, and the children loved to play around it. As they were doing so, Bertie, who was ten years old, suddenly called to his brother.

"Willie, come and look at this!" he said, pointing to a notice stuck on the window of a doctor's house just opposite the cabstand.

Willie ran across, and both boys read the notice.

LOST

Valuable Persian Cat.
Anyone returning same to
this address will receive
15 shillings reward.

A fever of excitement seized the boys. Fancy! Fifteen shillings reward! Why, that was the very amount they had asked Jesus to send them. They could almost feel the money in their pockets. Now they could stay! Wouldn't mother be pleased! The only real difficulty, of course, was to find the lost cat.

"We must find it!" said Willie, all eagerness.

"We are going to find it!" said Bertie.

But where could it be? It might be anywhere in Bath, for all they knew, and they had very little time to search, as they were due to leave for home in an hour or two.

All along the street they talked about the possibility of finding this precious cat. One moment it seemed impossible; the next they almost felt it purring in their arms.

They had not gone far when a sound from a dark corner brought them both to a standstill, dumb with excitement and surprise.

"Meow! Meow!"

Willie looked at Bertie, and Bertie looked at Willie. Could it—could it be?

They peered down into the area whence the sound had come. To be sure, there was a cat at the bottom. They ran down the steps and found themselves face to face with a beautiful big Persian cat. Indeed, it was so big that neither of the boys could pluck up courage enough to touch it.

"It must be the doctor's cat!" they cried together. "But how shall we get it back to him?"

"You stay here and watch it," said Bertie, "while I run back to the house."

The doctor's house was only a short distance away, and in a few moments Bertie was back again with the doctor's servant. Yes! It was the cat that had been lost.

In great glee the boys returned to their mother to tell how Jesus had answered their prayer, and that now they could attend all the meetings.

The next day they visited the doctor, who gladly handed them the reward and thanked them for helping him to find his cat. Mother was able to cancel the arrangements to return home, and they all stayed until the meetings closed.

Isn't it wonderful what Jesus will do to answer little boys' prayers?

And can you wonder that both Willie and Bertie are missionaries for Jesus in Africa today?

Agatha's Apple

Now you will be good while I'm out, won't you, Agatha?" said Mamma. "I must run down to the store for just a few minutes."

"Yes, Mamma," said Agatha. "May I push my doll carriage down the garden?"

"Certainly," said Mamma. "Good-by, dearie; Mamma won't be long."

And with that Mamma was off, and Agatha began to fix her dolls in her carriage ready for their stroll outside.

Now it happened that there were four very fine old apple trees in Agatha's garden. They had been there for years and years, and no one really knew who had planted them. They were great big trees, almost as high as the house, and every year they bore heaps of sweet, delicious apples.

Most of the apples had been

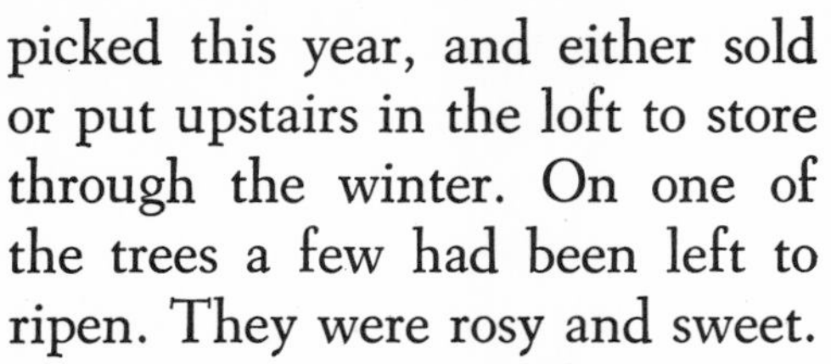

picked this year, and either sold or put upstairs in the loft to store through the winter. On one of the trees a few had been left to ripen. They were rosy and sweet.

As Agatha reached this particular tree with her large family of dolls, her eyes caught sight of the apples.

"I thought Mamma had picked all the apples," she said to herself. "She must have missed some of them by mistake."

Then she told her dolls about them. "Look at the lovely apples," she said. "Aren't they pretty? Would dolly like one to eat?"

Of course, by "dolly" Agatha really meant herself, for the more she looked at those big red apples, the more she thought she would like to taste one.

Standing by the tree was a very tall stepladder, and Agatha began to wonder whether it would be safe to go up it.

"It will be all right," she said to herself. "Mamma won't know anything about it, 'cause I can eat apples very quickly."

She put one foot on the ladder, then another. Slowly she climbed upward, holding on tightly to the sides. Soon she was up among the apples. Then she turned round to find the biggest one that she had seen from the ground. Ah, there it was. What a beauty! She really must have that one.

The apple was rather a long way off for her little arms, and Agatha had to let go of the ladder and hold on to a branch of the tree with one hand while she tried to loosen the apple with the other.

For some reason or other the apple did not come off as easily as Agatha had expected. Perhaps it was not quite ripe yet. At any rate she had to pull very hard. In doing so she leaned rather too far forward, and the apple suddenly broke off and dropped to the ground. Agatha fell off the ladder into the tree and slid down a branch until she was caught in a fork about six feet from the ground.

Unable to reach the ladder, she started to cry.

You should have heard the noise! Of course the poor little mite was very much frightened, thinking that perhaps she might fall again and hurt herself.

"Mamma! Mamma! Mamma!"

Mamma was halfway down the street when she heard the screams coming from her back garden, and she ran the rest of the way home as fast as she could.

Imagine her surprise when she saw one of her special rosy apples on the ground and another sort of apple hanging up there in the middle of the tree with a pink dress, two waving arms, and two kicking legs.

DON
NELSON

"What are you doing up there, Agatha?" she cried.

"Boo-hoo-hoo!" replied poor little Agatha. "Take me down, take me down!"

Of course Mamma quickly brought the ladder across and lifted Agatha gently from her very uncomfortable resting place.

"I'm so sorry—boo—hoo—hoo!" wailed Agatha. "I didn't mean to. I was only smelling the apples—boo—hoo—hoo! You won't spank me, will you, Mamma? You won't, will you?"

Mamma didn't spank her, because she was so glad her little girl hadn't fallen down and broken her back, but she did take her indoors and tell her that there is a verse in the Old Testament which says, "Be sure your sin will find you out."

Agatha listened quietly while Mamma talked about it, and was much interested as she told of all the trouble that had come because, once upon a time, another "little girl" had been tempted to take a lovely fruit in the Garden of Eden.

When Mamma had finished, they both knelt down, and Agatha prayed this little prayer: "Dear Jesus, thank You for keeping me safe when I fell off the ladder, and help me not to try to take apples off the tree any more, and help me always to do what Mamma says, and make me a good girl, for Jesus' sake. Amen."

Then they kissed each other and each ate half the apple.

Angels Without Wings

"What a beautiful picture!" exclaimed Peggy as she looked at the picture in her new book. "What are the children doing?"

"Don't you see?" said Big Sister. "They are picking flowers, and have wandered far away from home to the edge of a great precipice. Another step, and they will fall over it and be killed."

"But the angel won't let them," said Peggy.

"That's right; God has sent an angel just in time to hold them back and keep them safe," said Big Sister.

"Won't they be happy when they turn round and see that beautiful angel!"

"Perhaps they won't see him, though."

"Why not?"

"Because angels have a way of disappearing after they have done kind deeds."

"I wish I could see one," said Peggy.

"Someday you will," replied Big Sister, "for when Jesus comes back, He will bring hosts of shining angels with Him."

"Where are they all now?" asked Peggy.

NTING BY HARRY ANDERSON

sends His strong and beautiful angels to h over and protect those who love Him.

"Some are in heaven, and some are here all around us. God sends them to look after us just as He sent one to care for the little children in the picture. We cannot see them, but they can see us. When we are good they are happy; and when we are bad they weep. Jesus said they rejoice every time a sinner repents."

"Sometimes," said Peggy, shyly, "Mamma calls me a little angel."

"Not very often, I think," said Big Sister.

"Oh, yes, she does," replied Peggy perkily.

"Well, we can all be angels without wings," said Big Sister. "We think of angels as being all that is good and kind, loving and beautiful; and when we are like that, it's no wonder we are mistaken for angels! If we just had wings, no one would know the difference. Do you know anybody like that?"

Peggy thought for a moment. "Well, there's Auntie and old Mrs. Goodyear and—er—my friend Bessie and—er——"

"What about Mamma?"

"Oh, well, of course, Mamma. She is always looking after us just like the angel in the picture, isn't she?"

"Yes," said Big Sister, "and think of all the things she does for us all day long—cooking our food, mending our clothes, looking after us when we are sick, helping us with our lessons, taking us for treats, giving us presents—what would we do without her?"

"Oh, yes," said Peggy, "Mamma is the best angel; I wonder she hasn't grown wings and flown away a long time ago."

Just then there was a creaking sound from the armchair at the other end of the room. A head popped up from behind a newspaper and said, "And what about Daddy?"

"Oh, Daddy dear! We didn't know you were there!" cried Peggy and Big Sister as they dashed pell-mell across the room.

"Of course you are an angel, too, Daddy, but"—and two pairs of hands felt his back vigorously—"YOU haven't any wings yet."

How Donald Missed His Dinner

"Donald!"

Daddy shouted again, but no answer came.

"Where *is* the boy?" asked Daddy.

"It is so tiresome," said Mamma, quite annoyed; "dinner will be all spoiled."

"Well, we will go without him if he doesn't come soon," said Daddy.

Donald was always forgetting something. In the morning he would forget where he had left his shoes the night before. Then he would forget where he had laid his cap. He would leave books at home which he should take to school, and leave books at school which he should bring home. But his chief trouble was in keeping time. Although he had been given a fine new watch on his last birthday, still he forgot to look at it when it was most necessary that he should.

Just now he was wandering far away along the shore, intent only on his shrimping net. Nothing else interested him at all. He had been told to return without fail by a quarter to one, so that the family could all go back in the car for dinner.

But Donald was so happy and contented that he completely forgot his promise to return. He was out of sight of the rest of the party, and no one knew where he had gone. Father, Mother, Sister, Brothers—all called their loudest, but in vain. No Donald could be seen or heard anywhere.

"Where can he be?" asked Mamma, somewhat alarmed. "Do you think he could have hurt himself?"

"No, I don't," said Daddy. "It's just a little more of his old trouble. He has become interested in something and forgotten his promise. I'm going home."

"What, and leave him behind?" asked Mamma.

"Poor Donald," said Sister.

"Serves him right," said Brother.

"I want my dinner," pleaded Little Brother.

"Jump in the car," said Daddy.

"Oh," said Mamma, "I don't like to go and leave him behind."

"I don't either," said Daddy, "but he will have to learn sometime that he must keep his promises."

"Won't you have another look for him?" pleaded Sister. "It will take just a moment."

"All right," replied Daddy, "I'll look once more."

Leaving the others in the car, Daddy searched again and called for Donald at the top of his voice. But no Donald appeared. When Daddy returned to the car, there was a very determined look on his face. Not a word more would he say on the subject. He stepped on the gas and made for home and dinner.

It was a very nice dinner, but somehow no one seemed to enjoy it very much. Every now and then someone said, "I wish Donald was here," or "Wouldn't Donald like this?" and Little Brother kept repeating, "We must save some for Donald, mustn't we?"

It was two hours later before they all got back to the beach again. As the car drew up in the parking place, Little Brother shrieked, "I see him, I see him!"

Donald was there all right. He had come back in his own good time, and found everybody gone. Never in all his life had he felt so desolate and lonesome. And they had all gone to dinner! Dinner! The very thought of it had made him ravenously hungry. He had pictured all the good things the others were eating, and had become hungrier and hungrier. Then, guessing that everybody would return after dinner, he had

laid himself down beside a boat and tried to forget his troubles.

Donald was still gazing up into the sky when he was roused by the joyous rush of feet toward him.

"So here you are, after all," said Sister. "I am so glad you are all right."

"We had a fine dinner," said Brother. "You missed something, I can tell you, by being late."

Donald tried to look as if that didn't matter at all, and that he had never felt the slightest pang of hunger.

Daddy now appeared on the scene.

"We were sorry to leave you, Don," he said, "but you'll have to learn someday that keeping promises on time is a most important matter."

"It seems so," said Donald.

"It is most important," repeated Daddy.

Just then Little Brother crept close to Donald and whispered in his ear.

"I've brought you some of my dinner," he said. "It's done up in my handkerchief in my trouser pocket."

"You dear!" exclaimed Donald. "I won't forget that, anyway."

And the fact is he didn't forget the lesson either.

Where the Grass Grows Longer

"Who wants to earn some pennies for his missionary box?" asked Daddy.

"I do," said Morris.

"And I," said Monica eagerly.

"What do you want us to do?" they asked together.

"Something in the garden," said Daddy. "I have some plants coming in from the nursery, and I must have two borders by the lawn dug this afternoon. Do a good job, and there'll be a quarter each for your boxes."

"Good!" cried Morris, who loved digging. "Let's start now."

Monica didn't like it quite so much, but was willing enough to join in, especially with such an incentive. Both had forks of their own, nice little forks, just the right size for them, and getting these out of the shed, they were soon busily at work turning over the soil.

"I'll be done first," said Morris.

"No, you won't," retorted Monica.

And away they raced.

By and by Daddy came out to see how they were getting on.

"You do look busy," he said. "You will have to hurry, though, for I'm going to start setting the plants right away."

He started on the side where Morris was digging.

"This is excellent," he said. "You *are* digging this well. You have put your fork in as far as it would go, I can see. And you've taken the weeds out, too! That's a good boy. You will make a wonderful gardener."

Presently Daddy passed over to the other flower bed. But his smiles soon faded away.

"Hello!" he exclaimed, "what's this, Monica? You seem to have done a lot more than Morris, but what are those tufts of green sticking up here and there?"

"Must be one or two weeds, Daddy."

"One or two! Why, there are dozens of them. I think you must have been only scratching the top. Why, see, I can't get my trowel in more than three or four inches. That isn't the way to work."

Monica looked rather crestfallen.

"Perhaps we had all better take five minutes' rest," said Daddy. "Then we can start this bit over again; for my little plants would all die if I put them in here now."

"I'm not going to dig it again," said Monica.

"Well, let's have a rest," said Daddy.

So they all sat down on a box to take a "breather."

"Let me tell you a story while we're resting," said Daddy.

"That's better than digging," answered Monica.

"It's a good story," continued Daddy, "and it's about a man who dug his piece of land very well. Outside my office there is a large plot of grass. You may have seen it when you were over there the other day. During the first world war that plot was divided up among a number of men, and they were allowed to dig it up and plant it with vegetables. I remember what a job we had taking off the grass and then digging the ground for the first time. How we all worked! It was terribly hard, much harder than the job you have had this afternoon.

"For two or three years we dug and fertilized the land, planted our seeds, and gathered our crops. Then came peace. Food became easier to obtain, and we were all glad enough to give up our gardens and allow the farmer to come and plow the land and sow it again with grass for the cattle.

"To most people today that plot seems just an ordinary piece of grass, but, unknown to them, something wonderful happens there every year."

"What can it be?" asked Morris, as Daddy paused. "I've never heard of anything wonderful happening there."

"Very few know of it," replied Daddy, "but it happens all the same, with unfailing regularity, and probably will for many years to come."

"You are making me curious," said Monica.

"I'll tell you," said Daddy. "In the early summer, just before the hay is cut, a section of the grass, in shape just like one of the old gardens, grows several inches higher than all the rest of the field."

"Why is that?" asked Morris.

"Ah," said Daddy, "that long grass is a memorial to the hard and thorough work of the man who cultivated the land beneath it during the first world war."

"Was that you, Daddy?" asked Monica with a perky little smile.

"No, indeed, dear; I wish it had been. No, it was a Mr. Hammond. I remember how, early and late, he would work on his garden, digging it deeply and burying in it loads and loads of fertilizer. Men who smiled at him then for taking so much trouble with his garden have forgotten all about it, but God and nature never forget; and now, after all these years, the long grass rises every summer to tell the world that here worked a faithful and thorough man."

There was a moment or two of silence as Daddy finished. It was broken by Monica.

"Daddy," she said, her eyes dancing with eagerness, "I think I'll dig my piece over again, after all."

When the Well Dried Up

Rene was so thirsty. There was not a drop of water to be found anywhere. For many, many days there had been no rain. Not a cloud had crossed the sky, and the fierce African sun had scorched the whole land over hundreds of square miles. The rivers and streams had dried up, and now at last the deep well close to the farmhouse had run dry.

Rene's Daddy did not know what to do. He had worked very hard for many years to build up that home and to develop his land. Now it seemed that he was about to lose everything. His crops were withering away, and worse still, his cattle were parched with thirst, for there was no water to give them. What could he do?

Calling his family together, he told them how serious the situation was, and that he was going to ask Jesus to send rain.

So they all knelt down—Mother, Daddy, Rene, and her baby sister—and together they prayed as they had never prayed before. Father and Mother both prayed very earnestly that Jesus somehow would send rain to save the crops and to spare the herds of cattle.

When it came Rene's turn to pray, she did not say just what Mother and Father had said. She said, "Dear Jesus, if You don't send rain, please send some water into the well."

Daddy smiled, because he couldn't see how water could come into the well if it didn't rain. But Rene did not think about that. She believed that Jesus could do anything; and when they all got up off their knees, she said she was quite sure that Jesus was going to answer her prayer.

Father and Mother went about their various tasks around the home, but Rene disappeared. She had gone to the well to watch what Jesus would do.

She pulled and pushed at the cover, and finally succeeded in moving it enough so that she could look down. But the well was so deep and dark that she could see nothing at all. Picking up a stone, she dropped it in and listened intently. There was a moment of breathless waiting. Then—— "Splash!"

The next instant she was off to the house as fast as her legs could run.

"Jesus has sent the water!" she cried. "Jesus has sent the water!"

Father wouldn't believe it, but came running to the well to see, with Mother and the farm workers close behind. He dropped in another pebble, and there was another splash.

A moment later he had the pump working, and out from the well there was soon pouring a stream of clear, cold water.

How happy and thankful they all were! And do you know, from that day to this, that well has never run dry. Of course, some people say, "It just happened so." But little Rene knows better. She says Jesus sent the water in the well and answered a little girl's prayer, and I believe she is right.

A Bright Idea

Iris and Elsie were always getting bright ideas. You might see them whispering together behind the big armchair in the dining room, or under the stairs, or in the coal cellar. Then there would be a yell and a rush to find Mother.

"Mamma!" they would cry, "we've got such a bright idea. We would like to——"

Then they would tell Mother their new plan, perhaps for a new game, or perhaps for something to do at school. Mother did not always agree with the new ideas, and some of them, she said, were pure mischief. But now and then the two little girls thought of something really bright and good.

This particular morning they had been talking together in whispers under a tree in the garden for quite a long time. Presently, with happy shrieks, they came rushing across the lawn into the kitchen where Mother was peeling the potatoes for dinner.

"Mamma!" they cried, "we've such a bright idea."

"And what is it this time?" asked Mother.

"We want you to lend us some money."

Mother smiled at that.

"But I haven't any to lend," she said.

"But won't Daddy give you some more?"

"What for?"

"We want to sow some seeds in the garden, and earn some money for the missionaries, as other children do," said Iris.

"Why, Iris, where did you get that happy idea?" asked Mother, as she finished the potatoes.

"Why, at the children's meeting last week a missionary told about some little girls who grew mustard and cress for missions, and we want to do the same. They made lots of money."

Well, Mother gave in; and when Daddy came home, she persuaded him to lend the children twenty-five cents each to buy the garden seed they needed.

Next day Iris and Elsie were as busy as real gardeners. Daddy told them what to do, and dug up a small piece of ground for them. Then they leveled it and raked it over and over again until there wasn't a stone to be seen. When the plot was just right they scattered their seed and raked it over nicely and left it to grow.

In the morning they did not need calling, for each was eager to be out first to see whether anything had started to grow yet.

And a good thing it was that they went out so early, for there, right in the middle of the nicely raked patch, were three big birds scratching and having a fine feed of the unsprouted seeds.

"You naughty, naughty birds!" cried the children, shooing them away.

They found that the birds had done a great deal of damage, and they had to get some more seed to make up for what had been eaten. This time, however, Mamma let them have some mosquito netting to stretch over the garden until the plants were growing well.

In a short time the seeds began to throw out tiny little shoots. A little while later, it seemed almost in a night, up

jumped the little green leaves.

It was such fun to watch the plants growing! Of course they had to be watered, but that was no trouble at all. The only danger was that the plants might get drowned, they were watered so much.

Up, up, up grew the tiny plants, all so thick together. What a wonderful show it was! It seemed as if God must be helping these seeds to grow especially well because they were going to be a great help to the missionaries.

In a few weeks from the day the seed was sown, Daddy said it was nearly time to cut the greens.

What a moment of joy it was when clip, clip, clip went the scissors through the white stalks, cutting off the seeds, roots, and soil. And what greater joy when, with the mustard and cress neatly packed in a basket, the children marched up to the house to sell it to Mamma!

Yes, Mamma bought it. Then the children purchased some more seed, and sowed again. When this grew up, they had so much mustard and cress that they had to sell some to the lady who lived next door. Then they sowed again, and by and by they had so much that they had to ask the grocer to buy some. Each time they sold some mustard and cress they put some of the money away in a box, which they resolved not to open until the missionary came again to the children's meeting.

That was in about six months, but at last the day came. Tense excitement prevailed when the box was opened. There were several quarters in it, some dimes, and many nickels and pennies. After the service the children took the money up to the missionary and told him it was to help tell the little boys and girls in foreign lands about Jesus. "Thank you so much," he said, "but where did you get all this?"

Iris and Elsie paused and blushed. Then Iris, who was a little older and bigger, said, "It came out of a bright idea." And then, of course, they told the missionary all about it, and he told the story to other little boys and girls, so they would have some bright ideas too.

Daddy and the Ducks

Daddy had taken his two little girls down to the pond in the park. There were many kinds of lovely ducks in the pond—gray ducks, brown ducks, and white ducks. They swam easily over to where the children were.

"Daddy," said Polly thoughtfully as she threw a piece of bread to one of the ducks and watched the bird gobble it up, "why are ducks?"

"Because," said Daddy, "God made them."

"But why did God make them?" asked Patsy.

"Because—er—" hesitated Daddy, "because God thought He would like to have some ducks."

"Are they good ducks or bad ducks?" asked Polly.

"Very good ducks indeed," said Daddy.

"How do you know?" asked Patsy.

"Don't you see," said Daddy, "how they eat all the food that is put before them without grumbling? See, they eat greens and potatoes and bread, and never grumble a bit."

"But I am not a duck," said Patsy knowingly.

"No, but you are Daddy's ducky-daddles, and you must be just as good as these pretty ducks in the pond."

The Last Leaf on the Tree

"Now, Francis, let us go into the dining room and play some games," said Freda to her little guest.

It was Freda's birthday, and she had invited Francis, the boy who had just come to live next door, to have lunch with her.

"Let's play the games in the kitchen," suggested Francis. "Don't let's go in the dining room."

"But why?"

"Because the old lady is in there," said Francis, "and——"

"The 'old lady'!" exclaimed Freda. "Why, that's my Grandma."

"Sorry," said Francis penitently, "but won't she grumble if we make a noise?"

"Oh dear no!" said Freda. "You don't know Grandma; she loves to have us play where she is. You come and see."

So they went into the dining room, and Freda introduced Francis to Grandma. She greeted him with such a cheery smile that his fears were banished at once.

"You don't mind our playing in here, do you, Grandma?" said Freda.

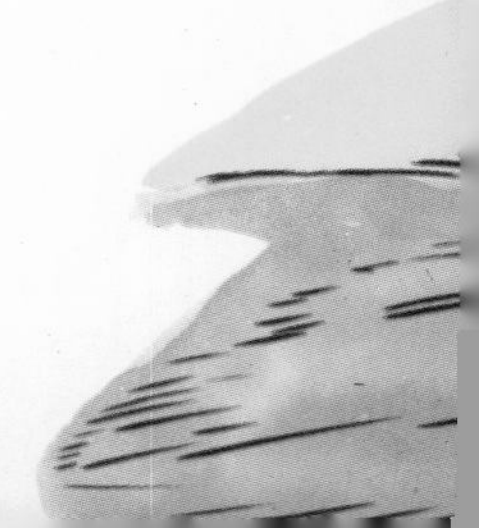

"Mind?" echoed Grandma. "I should mind if you didn't. I love to see you play. It makes me feel young again myself."

So, with Mother's help, the children were soon having great fun playing blindman's buff, hunt the thimble, and all the other games that children love to play at birthday parties. Grandma joined in as best she could from the security of her armchair, and didn't mind the noise a bit, not even when Freda, as "blindman," chased Francis round and round her chair.

At last the children grew tired of their frolic, and came to sit down by the fire at Grandma's knee.

"Tell us a story, Grandma," begged Freda. "You have such lovely stories to tell."

"A story?" questioned Grandma. "What shall it be about this time?"

"About when you were a little girl," suggested Freda, who

never seemed to grow tired of listening to Grandma on this subject.

"That was a long, long time ago," said Grandma, "but I still remember some of the things I used to do when I was young. I've told you lots about them before, but there's one thing I was especially thinking about this afternoon before you dear children came in."

"Do tell us about that, then," said Freda eagerly.

"I'm afraid it isn't a real story," replied Grandma, "and it is a little sad."

"That is all the better," answered Freda, making herself a little more comfortable. "I like sad stories best of all."

"Then I will tell you," said Grandma. "As I was sitting here this afternoon, I began to think of all the little children I used to know when I was a little girl, and of my own dear brothers and sisters."

"Did you have brothers and sisters?" asked Freda. "I never knew that."

"Why, yes," said Grandma. "And we all loved one another very much. We had a dear Mother and were such a happy family. We went to school together—such as it was—and we loved to romp and play just as you do. Times were harder in some ways then, and we didn't have the comforts that folks have nowadays, but we got a good deal of joy out of life."

Grandma paused and sighed a little as her mind wandered back over the days that were gone forever. Then she went on.

"The years have rolled by very quickly, but as they have passed I have seen all the little children who were with me in school grow up from boys and girls to manhood and womanhood. I went to many of their weddings, and afterward, when they became Daddies and Mommies, I nursed and played with their children. Still the years passed, and one by one they have grown tired and fallen asleep. Gradually, as in the autumn time the old leaves fall from the trees, so they too have passed away, and I was thinking this afternoon that of all our happy little group of children in the old schoolhouse I alone am left. And there came back to my mind that beautiful verse of the poet:

" 'If I should live to be
The last leaf on the tree
In the spring,
You may laugh, as I do now,
At the old, forsaken bough,
Where I cling.' "

Again Grandma paused. The children were very silent, and there were tears in Freda's eyes.

"Grandma mustn't feel lonely," she said lovingly.

"Oh, no," said Grandma bravely. "I am not a bit. That is

why I'm so glad to have you come and play around me. *You* wouldn't let anyone get lonely."

Just then there was a knock at the front door. It was someone to say that it was time Francis came home because it was his bedtime.

On the way out to the hall Francis whispered in Freda's ear, "I'm glad we didn't stay in the kitchen for our games, aren't you?"

"Yes," said Freda. "Isn't Grandma beautiful? It would be too bad to make her feel she wasn't wanted, wouldn't it?"

"Yes," said Francis. "I'm coming to see her again, if I may."

And perhaps there are some other old folks here and there who are thinking about "the last leaf on the tree," and secretly longing for the touch of sympathy and love that you can give.

How Not to Help Mother

Daisy was looking about for something to do while Mamma talked to the neighbor. Neighbors can talk quite a long time, as you may know.

"I wish I could do something to help Mamma," she said to herself, "but all the jobs seem to have been done. The dishes are washed and the table is cleared, and I don't want to do any more dusting. I think I'll go out into the garden."

So out she went, and before long spied the birdbath, which had nearly dried up.

"I know," she said, "I'll fill up the birdbath. That will be something useful, anyhow."

Then she suddenly remembered that Mamma had said that on no account was she to play with the water, for she always got wet.

"But I'm sure she wouldn't call this playing with the water," she thought to herself. "This is really helping. I'll get the can."

So she found the can, put in as much water as she felt was safe, and carried it over to the bath. It was a little heavy to lift,

but she managed it all right, and then went back for some more. This time she brought a little less, so that she would be sure not to spill any.

Slowly the shallow bath was filled.

"I think it will take just another can," she said, going back to the faucet once more. Soon she returned, and mounting the box she had been using to stand on, began to pour it in.

But there was one important thing she had failed to notice. The bath, unfortunately, was uneven, so that while on one side it appeared to be only partly full, on the other it was already almost overflowing. Consequently when Daisy cheerfully tipped in the last canful, it started to pour over the side all down her nice clean dress. At first she did not notice it, but as it soaked through her dress and then dripped onto her bare legs, she started back in such a fright that she dropped the can and fell off the box into the flower bed.

"Oh dear! What will Mamma say?" she said, picking herself up and looking down at her wet, mud-splashed dress and dirty shoes.

"Yes, indeed!" Daisy recognized Mamma's familiar voice.

"I was only trying to help you by filling the birdbath, Mamma," said Daisy. "I didn't mean to make all this mess."

"You never do mean to," said Mamma. "But Daisy, when will you remember that the best way to help Mamma is always to do what she says? Come on in and change your dress."

Daisy went, and was given plenty of time to think it over while Mamma found her some clean, dry clothes.

How Boss Came Home

I have come to the conclusion that there must be hundreds and hundreds of lost dogs around. Every few days some boy or girl writes to tell me how his precious pup ran away, and how, in some wonderful way, it turned up again.

Perhaps you would like to hear some of these interesting stories that children have told me about their pets. The first is "How Boss Came Home."

Bert, aged eight, was the proud owner of a small brown-and-white terrier called Boss, which he loved dearly. One day, after Father had gone to work, Boss decided to go too. On and on he went for several miles, following a mountain road toward a clearing in the woods where Father was building a new house.

Suddenly Father looked back and there was Boss following close behind him.

"Why, Boss," he said, "what are you doing here? You shouldn't have come all this way.
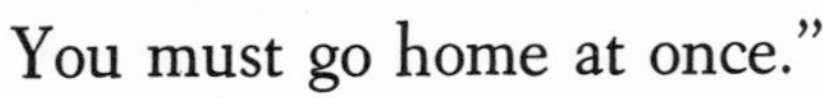
You must go home at once."

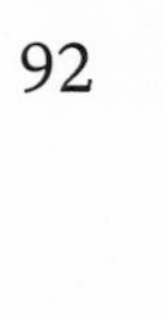

But Boss didn't want to go home. He sat down and looked up pleadingly into Father's face.

"Go home, Boss!" said Father again sternly.

Boss got up and turned toward home, his tail between his legs.

Father went on his way and for-

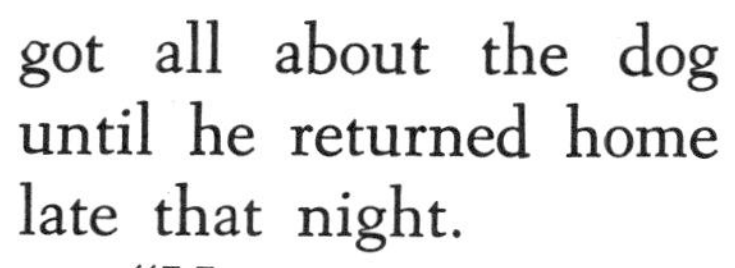

got all about the dog until he returned home late that night.

"Have you seen Boss?" cried Bert, running out to meet him. "He hasn't been around here all day."

Then Father happened to remember.

"Sure," he said. "He followed me up the mountain this morning, but I sent him back. Hasn't he come home yet?"

"No," said Bert, "we

haven't seen him at all. Maybe he has come to some harm in the woods or maybe he can't find his way home."

Bert was worried and so was Father, for the weather was cold, far too cold for a little dog to be out all night.

When Bert went to bed he prayed for Boss. "Jesus," he said, "please look after poor little Boss. Keep him from dying of cold on the mountain and bring him back safe to me."

When morning came, there was a loud yapping on the porch underneath Bert's bedroom. Bert awoke with a start and ran downstairs. It was Boss, of course, all safe and sound and none the worse for his adventure.

Queenie Disappears

The next story was sent to me by a little girl called Patricia, and a very nice letter she wrote, too. Her dog is a purebred springer spaniel, but she forgot to tell me its name. So I'll call the dog Queenie, and hope I am not far wrong.

Well, Patricia, her Daddy, and her brother rode their bicycles out to a ranch where they could rent horses for a ride over the hills. Queenie went too, trotting along beside them. All went well until the time came for them to turn back from their long horseback ride. Then somebody noticed that Queenie was not there. They called and called in vain. They thought that she might have gone back

to the ranch by herself, but when they finally arrived there, Queenie was nowhere to be found. They all became anxious and began calling, "Queenie!" as loud as they could. Still there was no sign of the dog. She had disappeared. Daddy became so worried that he even phoned to the nearest radio station, asking the announcer to broadcast the news that the dog had been lost. Then Patricia and her brother began to pray, asking God to help them find poor lost Queenie.

Hours passed. Still the dog was missing. Then they all decided to go out over the hills again and search the whole district. Patricia and her brother went in one direction, Father in another. On and on they walked. Father even climbed away up to the top of the highest hill, so that he could look all around the countryside; but the familiar form of their beloved Queenie was nowhere to be seen.

As he came down again he felt quite discouraged. Then the thought came to him, "Why shouldn't I say a little prayer for Queenie, just as the children have done?"

Father dropped on one knee and asked the Lord to help him find the lost dog.

When he opened his eyes, what do you suppose he saw?

Queenie, of course! There she was, right in front of him, wagging her tail so hard it's a wonder it didn't drop off. How glad they all were to see her again!

A Tale of Three Pups

Here is a story about another little girl who loved dogs. In fact, this little girl wanted a dog so very much that she had prayed for one for years. I know, for she told me so herself.

One day, some years ago, her Daddy had brought her a spaniel puppy so black and so pretty that she had called it Black Beauty; and she had said to herself, "Here is the answer to my prayers!" But it wasn't, for just then her Daddy had had to move to an apartment in a big city, where there was no room for dogs, not even for puppies, and poor, heartbroken Dorothy had had to give away her precious Black Beauty to one of the little neighbor girls.

But Dorothy prayed on, and some months later her Daddy moved to another city, where there was room for a dog. They had hardly arrived when a strange puppy wandered into the house.

"Now my prayers are answered!" cried Dorothy, and she named this puppy Gypsy. But it wasn't the answer to her prayers, for the very next night Gypsy ran away and never came back!

"Can't I ever have a puppy of my own?" said Dorothy as she sobbed out her prayers that night. "I've prayed and prayed for one so long."

It so happened that a kind lady living nearby heard about

the little girl who had been praying for a puppy and who never seemed to be able to get one to keep for her own. It happened, too, that this kind lady had more puppies than she needed, and she said to herself, "Why shouldn't I give one to this sad little girl?" And she selected a pretty one to take to her.

You can imagine how pleased Dorothy was when this kind neighbor placed the sweet little brown-and-white puppy in her arms. Dorothy thought it was a very wonderful puppy.

When I met Dorothy one day, I found her as happy as could be. "My prayers have really been answered at last," she told me.

"I am so glad," I remarked. "And what is the name of your third puppy?"

"Pepper," she said.

Now just think of that! What a name for a dog!

The Angel of the Books

What dreadful language you are bringing into this house, Tom," said Mother one day. "Why, even Joan and Jess are calling each other 'little beasts' and things like that. It's got to stop right now."

"Can't help it," said Tom, who had just started going to school. "All the boys call each other names."

"But you mustn't do it, Tom. You must be different and set the other boys a good example."

"Can't," said Tom. "They're all bigger than I am, and they won't listen to me."

"That may be," said Mamma, "but you don't need to use the same language as the other boys. Anyhow, you mustn't use it in this house; that's sure."

"Oh, rats!" said Tom.

"Tom!" exclaimed Mother. "That's the last time you will use such slang in speaking to me."

"Rats!" came a small echo from the dining room.

"There!" said Mother. "There's little Joan learning that from you now. I won't have it. The next time you use any of those idle words, you shall go to bed without any supper."

"Oh, shoot!" muttered Tom under his breath.

"That's enough," said Mother. "Up you go."

"But I was just going out to play football."

"Doesn't matter. It is much more important to learn that you must not use bad language."

Tom sauntered slowly upstairs and into his bedroom. More slowly still he undressed and got into bed. He didn't mind going to bed so much, but the fact that there was to be no supper was too much for him. Tears began to trickle down his cheeks. He tossed and turned, wiped his eyes, put the handkerchief under his pillow, and pulled it out again. At last he dozed off.

Hello! Who was this in his bedroom? He rubbed his eyes and sat up, very much frightened.

"Say, who are you?" he exclaimed.

"I am the Angel of the Books," said the visitor.

"Books!" gasped Tom. "What books?"

"The books of heaven," said the angel. "I record every idle word that men speak."

"Good Lor'," said Tom.

"That also will be written down."

"Mustn't I say that?"

"It is very wrong. Have you not read, 'Thou shalt not take the name of the Lord thy God in vain'?"

"I'm sorry," said Tom. "I promise I won't say it any more."

"You will not be able to," said the angel. "For all the bad words you've said you must be silent for a long time."

The angel disappeared. Tom, very much frightened, tried to call Mother and tell her about what he had seen, but he could not speak. It was terrible. He wanted to tell Mother how sorry

PAINTING BY RUSSELL HARLAN

"I am the Angel of the Books," said the vis
"You must be silent a long time."

he was for being rude to her, but he couldn't say a word. He remembered how mean he had been to his auntie, and wanted to go and ask her pardon, but not a word could he utter. Then he thought of dear little Jess and Joan. How he wanted to go and tell them a story, and be nice to them to make up for teasing them so much, but he could not. Not a word would come from his lips.

"Oh dear!" he thought. "Shall I never be able to speak again?"

He saw Mother lying in bed very ill, and heard the doctor come and say how sick she was. He heard people come upstairs bringing fruit and flowers to cheer her up. He heard all the kind things they said to her. How he longed to go to her bedside and tell her he would try to be a good boy, and how he, too, wanted her to be well again, but his tongue would not move.

Ah! Here was the angel back again.

"I believe you have learned your lesson," said the Angel of the Books.

Tom nodded his head while the big tears ran down his face.

"If you promise to try hard never to use a bad word again," said the angel, "you may speak."

Tom nodded his head, the gift of speech returned, and the angel disappeared once more.

* * * * *

"What's the matter, dearie?" said Mother, bending over him.

"Oh, Mother dear!" cried Tom, "I've had such a wonderful and terrible dream. And I do love you so much, and I'll never, never use bad words again."

Teddy and the Tools

Teddy was sure he was going to be a carpenter when he grew up. He could not see a hammer without wanting to hit something with it. Whenever he could get any nails, he liked to hammer them into wood. He did not mind very much what wood it was, so long as it was soft wood. He did not like hard wood, for the nails just bent or fell out.

Teddy liked to mend things in his own way. Sometimes he would mend them quite well, as when his little brother's wheelbarrow lost a leg and he nailed it on again. He was quite proud of the job.

But sometimes he tried to mend things he should have left alone.

Now, Daddy had told him that he must not take any more nails or any more tools out of his shed. Indeed, Daddy had said that if Teddy *did* take any more things out of Daddy's shed, it would be a sorry day for Teddy.

But Teddy forgot. One day he saw that Mamma had put

a chair outside for Daddy to mend. The back was coming off, and Teddy said to himself, "I can mend that easily. I will give Daddy a surprise when he comes home from the office tonight."

So he took Daddy's hammer again, and Daddy's nails, and he nailed the back of the chair on again. Then he put the chair back in the dining room. But he did not notice that he had put in many more nails than were necessary, and that one of them had gone right through the wood.

So of course, when Daddy came home and sat down in the chair he did get a surprise, for he sat right down on the nail.

And then Teddy got a surprise too, for Daddy said he must learn not to be disobedient any more.

Margaret's New Shoes

Springtime was coming on, and Margaret, like every other little girl I know, wanted some new clothes, and particularly a new pair of shoes. She kept coaxing her Mamma to take her out shopping until at last Mamma said, "All right, dear, let's go." So off they went.

Coming to a shoe store, Margaret sat down in a chair and put her foot up on the stool, just as all the big people were doing. Along came a friendly lady who took off one of Margaret's old shoes and began to try on some of the new shoes.

How pretty they all were! So pretty indeed that Margaret couldn't tell which she wanted. At last, however, she decided to have a white pair, with straps, and Mamma said she thought Margaret had made a very good choice. Mamma then paid the bill, and the two walked out of the shop together, Margaret holding the precious parcel tightly under her arm, as happy a little girl as could be found in all the city. She had her new shoes at last! How envious her playmates would be!

Now they went to do some more shopping. Mamma thought that perhaps Margaret should have a new dress, or a new coat, to go with the lovely new shoes; so they went into a department store that had a great many things especially for little girls. It was crowded with people. In fact, there were so many other Mammas trying to buy things for their little girls that it was a long time before Margaret was able to get any attention at all.

At last an assistant came along, and with her help Margaret tried on this and that but without success. Nothing seemed to fit properly, and if anything did fit, then it was the wrong color or the wrong material. Finally Mamma said, "Perhaps we had better leave it for now and try another day." So they decided to leave.

As they stepped out on the street, Margaret cried, "My parcel! My parcel! Where is it?"

"I don't have it," said Mother. "Where can it be?"

It was nowhere to be found. They went straight back into the store to ask if anyone had seen a small parcel, but of course nobody had. There were too many people coming and going, and everyone was too busy thinking of his own things to bother

about one little parcel. Mamma left her name and address, in case someone might bring the parcel back, but with little hope of seeing it again.

Poor Margaret! How she wept! In fact, she cried all the way home. So upset was she that Mamma began to wonder if she should buy her another pair of shoes, but she didn't want to spend so much money just now.

When they reached home, Margaret was still in tears. "I did so want to have those new shoes!" she said. "They were so pretty, and I wanted to wear them to church next Sabbath."

"I'm so sorry, darling," said Mamma. "I wish we could do something about it, but what can we do?"

"Mamma," said Margaret, as she wiped her eyes once more —and she really said these very words—"Mamma, couldn't we ask Jesus to send them back just as it says in the *Bedtime Stories?*"

Mamma had been reading *Bedtime Stories* to Margaret every night for a long time, and now she, too, recalled some of the answers to children's prayers recorded there. So she answered, "Well, Margaret, I don't see why Jesus shouldn't do something special for you as He has for all those other children we have been reading about. Why not try? Why not tell Him about your new shoes?"

She did. As Margaret got down on her knees beside her bed that night, she said: "Dear Jesus, please make the person who took my shoes bring them back again. You see, my Mamma can't buy me another pair just now, and I do want them so much. Please, please, send them back to me."

Then, just like a little five-year-old, she got into bed and fell asleep.

Some time after that the telephone rang. It was a man at the department store. "I think we have your parcel," he said. "A customer who had picked it up by mistake has just brought it back." And he described the contents.

"That's right!" cried Mamma excitedly. "That's ours! I'll come and get it first thing tomorrow morning."

Seventeen Cowards

Bill came rushing into the house and flopped down in a chair, breathless. He looked scared out of his life.

At that moment Father came into the room, too. "Whatever's the matter, Bill?" he inquired anxiously.

"Oh, nothing," said Bill.

"Yes, there is," said Father. "I can tell by the look on your face. What has happened?"

"Oh, well, Dad," said Bill, wriggling uncomfortably in his chair, "you see, we were all playing ball up there on that vacant lot near old Mrs. Boliger's. You know where it is, Dad, about half a mile down the street from here."

"Yes, I know it well," said Father. "I used to play on it myself when I was a boy."

"Well, Dad, the ball——" hesitated Bill.

"I know what you are going to say," said Father. "The ball went through Mrs. Boliger's window."

"Well, yes, Dad. That's what happened. It was an accident, but how did you know?"

AINTING BY MANNING DE V. LEE

nteen boys were playing ball on the vacant lot near old Mrs. Boliger's.

"I just guessed," said Father. "But, say, Bill, why are you so scared?"

"I'm not really scared, Dad," said Bill, "but, you know, Mrs. Boliger is such a mean old woman. She makes such a fuss about things like that."

"Well, what did you all do after the window was broken?"

"We ran away."

"You ran away!"

"Yes."

"Well, how many boys were playing?"

"Seventeen."

"And you mean to tell me that all seventeen of you ran away, afraid of what some elderly woman might say to you?"

"Yes, Dad," said Bill, hanging his head a little.

"Well," said Father, "all I can say is that I think you were just seventeen cowards, that's all."

Bill didn't like that, but he knew in his heart that the charge was true. For a moment he tried to defend himself.

"But, Dad, that old Mrs. Boliger is so cranky," he said.

"It doesn't matter how cranky she is," said Father. "If you boys broke her window, you should have had the courage to go and tell her you did it, and offer to pay for the damage. Why, bless your heart, it wouldn't have cost more than a few cents apiece. By the way, who hit the ball that broke the window?"

Bill hesitated. "Er-er-er——" he began.

"Now come on," said Father. "There couldn't have been seventeen balls, nor could seventeen boys have smashed the window at once."

"That's right, Dad."

"Then who hit the ball that broke the window?"

"I did," said Bill, very crestfallen.

"I thought so," said Father, "only I wanted you to own up. And now, no matter what the others do, you must go at once to Mrs. Boliger's, tell her you are sorry and ask her how much the damage will be."

"I couldn't, Dad," cried Bill, truly alarmed. "I simply couldn't. She is such a dreadful crank."

"But you must," said Father severely. "It is the only proper thing to do. What is more, no boy of mine is going to be such a coward as not to apologize when he has done a thing like this. So get yourself cleaned up, and we'll go."

"You mean you are going to go with me?"

"Yes, I am going to go with you as far as Mrs. Boliger's front gate, and then you are going to go to the door and speak to her all by yourself."

"Oh, groans," Bill muttered to himself as he got off his chair and went to the bathroom to wash his hands and brush his hair.

By and by he came downstairs again, where Father was all ready, waiting for him. Together they set out for Mrs. Boliger's.

It wasn't a very happy journey; at least not for Bill. He couldn't have been more scared if he had been on his way to an examination, or to prison.

"Do I really have to go?" he asked after a while.

"I'm afraid you do," said Father. "There's really no other way. And you will feel a great deal happier when you have done the right thing."

Silence fell again. They walked on, Bill wishing that the distance might have been twenty miles, so Father would get tired and give up.

At last they turned a corner and came to the vacant lot where the accident had taken place. Mrs. Boliger's house was in full view, and so was the broken window.

"Here we are," said Father, as they reached the little white gate at the entrance to Mrs. Boliger's property. "I will wait here while you go to the house and speak to her. It is much better for you to do this little job alone. I shall be nearby if you need me."

There was nothing else for Bill to do now but go on alone, but as he went up the path he felt sure that Mrs. Boliger's eyes were watching him all the way.

And all the time he kept thinking to himself, "What will

she say when I tell her I was the one who broke her window?"

Bill rang the bell. It sounded loud and long, like the very knell of doom.

The door opened, and there stood Mrs. Boliger. To Bill's amazement she had a smile on her face. He had not expected that.

"How do you do?" she said in a kindly tone of voice. "What can I do for you?"

"Well—er—well—er," stuttered Bill, blushing all over, "I—er—I—er—am the boy who—er—hit the ball that—er

—broke your window this afternoon, and I am truly sorry."

Bill hesitated and then turned away a little as though he were waiting for a bomb to explode.

But it didn't. Instead he heard a very sweet voice saying, "I am proud of you, son. I have had my windows broken this way many, many times, but you are the very first boy who has ever come to tell me about it. You are a real little gentleman. You surely must have been brought up well. You must have a wonderful Father."

"Oh," said Bill, "that's my Dad over there. He happened to come along with me."

At this, of course, Father had to come up the path and join them.

"You have a fine boy here," said Mrs. Boliger. "In fact, I think he's the grandest boy I've ever met. You know, sir, no boy has ever come here before and spoken to me like this about breaking my windows."

"Well, Mrs. Boliger," said Father, "Bill and I would like to pay you for putting the glass in again."

"Oh dear, no," said Mrs. Boliger. "I wouldn't think of it. It's quite all right. I've mended so many before. And I wouldn't have this dear boy pay for one of my windows in any case."

Bill beamed with joy and pride.

They all talked together for a little while, and then Father and Bill said good-by and started for home.

"I suppose," said Father, "you aren't sorry you went to see her?"

"I should say not," said Bill. "Why, she was as nice as pie. I never would have dreamed that Mrs. Boliger could be like that. I wonder why the boys say that she is mean? She isn't a bit

mean. She couldn't have been kinder or more considerate."

"Boys say those things sometimes because they don't understand," said Father. "By the way, Bill, don't you feel better now since you have done the right thing, the brave thing?"

"Do I!" said Bill. "I could jump clear over the moon!"

Worm's Teeth

Mother knew that something had gone wrong just as soon as Martha came in the back door. Something seemed to tell her that the examination results had been announced, and Martha wasn't on the list. Yet she did not like to say anything for fear of what might happen.

"Any news?" she asked cautiously.

"Only bad news," said Martha, turning her head away and going upstairs.

In a few moments Mother followed her and, as she half expected, found Martha weeping disconsolately in her room.

"The exam?" asked Mother sympathetically.

Martha nodded.

"I tried so hard," she said, "and it's terrible to have failed. What shall I do? I feel like giving up everything. I simply can't go back to school."

And with that Martha broke into a fit of sobbing that made Mother want to cry, too.

"Martha," said Mother, after a while, "you don't need to feel so bad about it. I know you worked ever so hard, and it's just a pity that things have come out this way. But there, it isn't everybody that passes an examination the first time. If everybody did, why, the examiners would just make the examinations all the harder, so as to make sure somebody at least would fail. The best thing is to cheer up and resolve to try again and do better next time."

"Oh, I don't want to," wailed Martha. "I shall never be any good anyway."

"You mustn't say that," said Mother. "Why, some of the greatest men and women who ever lived were dreadful dunces at school. Some of them failed at their examinations over and over again. It isn't the fact of failing that matters, but whether or not we give up because we've failed. If after every failure we can set our will to try again, then victory is bound to come someday, and nothing will be impossible to us."

Still Martha could not stop weeping.

"It's no good," she sobbed. "Other people may be able to do that, but I can't. I just don't want to take any exam ever again. I know I would fail every time."

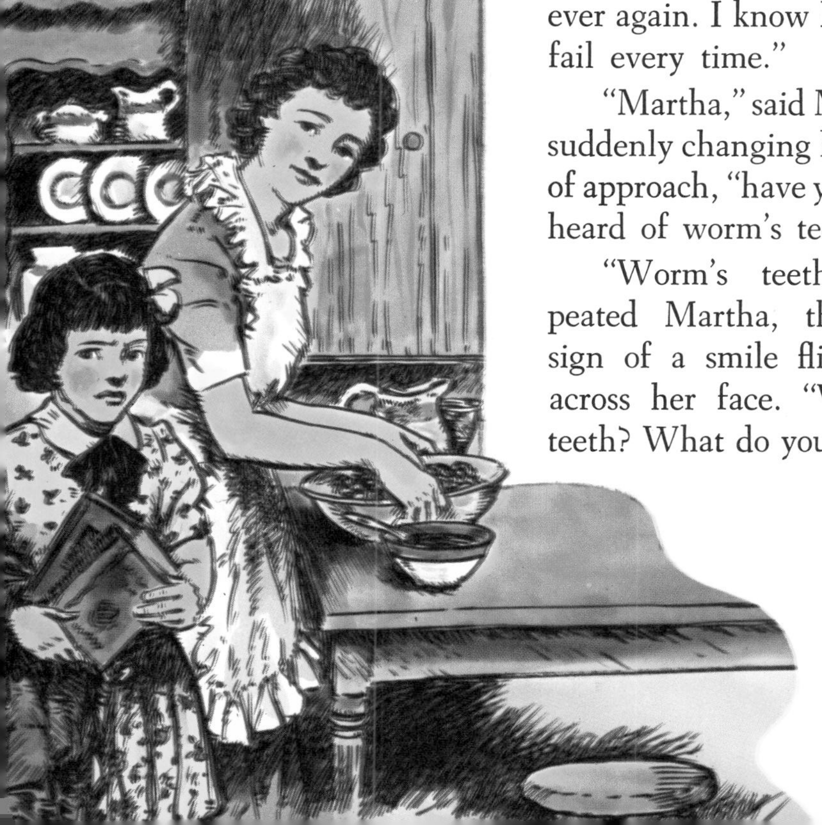

"Martha," said Mother, suddenly changing her line of approach, "have you ever heard of worm's teeth?"

"Worm's teeth?" repeated Martha, the first sign of a smile flickering across her face. "Worm's teeth? What do you mean,

Mother? And what has that to do with that wretched exam?"

"Well," said Mother, "they have a whole lot to do with it. If you will pass me your Bible, I will read you all about them."

"There you are," said Martha, passing her Bible to Mother with another faint smile; "but you won't find any worm's teeth in there."

"You wait a minute," said Mother, turning the pages rapidly until she found the forty-first chapter of Isaiah.

"Now, listen," she said. "I'm going to read verse ten first of all. There we have this beautiful promise of help in times of discouragement: 'Fear thou not; for I am with thee: be not dismayed; for I am thy God: I will strengthen thee; yea, I will help thee; yea, I will uphold thee with the right hand of My righteousness.'

"Isn't that beautiful? But again, in verse thirteen, we have these comforting words: 'I the Lord thy God will hold thy right hand, saying unto thee, Fear not; I will help thee.' Evidently God was trying to encourage His people not to give up, and not to despair because things had gone wrong.

"Then," went on Mother, "in verses fourteen and fifteen we read this extraordinary expression: 'Fear not, thou worm Jacob. . . . Behold, I will make thee a new sharp threshing instrument having teeth: thou shalt thresh the mountains, and beat them small, and shalt make the hills as chaff.' "

"Now I see the worm's teeth," smiled Martha.

"Yes," said Mother. "Isn't it a wonderfully inspiring promise? God knew that His people were feeling as small and worthless as a worm, thinking that they didn't count for anything at all. So He said, Cheer up! Trust in Me and try again, and I will give you teeth strong enough to eat mountains!"

“I never saw that in the Bible before,” exclaimed Martha. “It is a bit cheering, isn’t it?”

“I should say it is,” said Mother. “And I believe it was put there to encourage us just now. God brings us all sorts of experiences in this life to test and try us, but never to discourage us. He wants us to triumph over these seeming disasters. Every time we do so we shall grow stronger and stronger. We shall develop teeth of such power that they will bite through the biggest mountains of difficulty that may ever rise up to discourage us."

"Mother," said Martha, with a new light in her eyes, "do you know what I've just been thinking?"

"I think I can guess," said Mother, "but I'm not sure."

"Well," said Martha, "I just wish I could take that next exam tomorrow morning!"

Our Wonderful World

Did you ever stop to think what a wonderful world it is in which we live?

The fact is that Someone has packed it full of marvelous things, great and small.

Just think how big it is.

Do you know? Well, it is a great ball twenty-five thousand miles in circumference. That means that it must be about eight thousand miles through the center, from one side to the other. Now just think of that. The deepest oil well does not go down more than three or four miles. To make a hole right through, so that we could walk along a tunnel to our friends on the other side of the world, would be an immense and, indeed, an impossible task.

Over all the surface of the earth there are mighty oceans, lofty mountains, wide lakes, dense jungles, vast forests, and great expanses of desert. The oceans, lakes, and rivers teem with fish. The forests and jungles are alive with birds and beasts of all descriptions. Everywhere on land are plants and flowers innumerable. What a wonderful playground the world is for the people who live on it! And on that playground are nearly 3,000,000,000 human beings.

When you think of the world in this way, you say to yourself, "What a big place it is!" and you feel as small as a little ant in the garden crawling about over a pumpkin.

But, big though it seems to us, the world is only a little speck of dust in the great, wide universe.

Did you ever think you would like to pay a visit to the moon? On a clear evening it does not seem so very far away, and you have sometimes thought, perhaps, that a fast airplane would get you there quite soon. But it wouldn't. Even though your airplane traveled at 600 miles an hour, it would take you over two weeks to get there. Someday you may go there in a rocket-propelled spaceship, but that will take three or four days.

And if you were to try a trip to the nearest of the stars, you would die of old age scores of years before you began to get anywhere near it.

The stars, too, are bigger than our sun, and the sun is many times bigger than our world; yet all are moving swiftly and silently in mighty orbits through the realms of space.

Have you ever looked up in the sky on a calm, cloudless night? Of course you have. The heavens seem full of stars. But you can see only three thousand all together. But look through a small telescope, and you can see three million. Look through a larger telescope, and you can see endless millions more. And all of them are suns, radiating light and heat, many of them having worlds like ours revolving round them as we revolve round the sun.

How very small, then, we really are! That ant on the pumpkin makes us seem too big and important. We are more like a

speck of dust on a golf ball. The thought should humble us.

As we gaze on all these wonders of the universe, we are compelled to ask, Who made them? Who placed the stars in the sky? Who set them moving through the mighty universe?

Who makes them keep perfect time so that they never bump into one another? Who gave them the power to shine?

As we ask, we know that there can be only one answer. God made them. They did not create themselves. They did not evolve. They sprang suddenly into existence at the command of the Most High God. "By the word of the Lord were the heavens made; and all the host of them by the breath of His mouth." "For He spake, and it was done; He commanded, and it stood fast." Psalm 33:6, 9.

And what shall we do as we think of the greatness, the wisdom, and the power of the One who called these millions of stars into existence, set them all in motion, and keeps them all in place by His word? "O come, let us worship and bow down: let us kneel before the Lord our maker." Psalm 95:6.

But the greatest wonder of all concerning this world of ours is God's care for it. By comparison with the rest of His universe, it may be very small indeed, just like a marble in the Atlantic Ocean, but God loves it more than all the rest.

Why? Who can tell? We only know that He does. He tells us that He so loved our world "that He gave His only begotten Son, that whosoever believeth in Him should not perish, but have everlasting life." John 3:16.

Just think of that! Think of the infinite God in all His majesty and glory. Think of that little "speck of dust" on the "golf ball." Why should God love it? It can only be because He is infinitely wise and good; because His great heart of love is so full of understanding and compassion that it reaches out and touches every little life everywhere within His vast domain.

And perhaps God loves this world best of all because it alone fell into sin and yielded to the temptations of Satan. It

REE LIONS

es making our world, the sun and stars, made the beautiful trees, flowers, and baby s. Best of all, He made little boys and girls.

is said that a Mother loves the bad boy of the family best, not because she loves badness, but because she feels he needs the love most to bring him back to goodness and truth. So it must be with God. He loves us all, not because of our sins, but because He wants us to come back to Him.

We must never think we are too small for God to care for us. He made the stars, truly, but He painted the lily, too. He placed the great sun in the sky to send us light and heat across millions of miles of space, but He made the fireflies also. He set the moon on high to rule the night, but He gave to tiny fishes the power to light the darkest depths of the oceans. He reared up the mighty masses of the mountains, but He designed the wings of butterflies as well.

"O Lord, how manifold are Thy works! in wisdom hast Thou made them all: the earth is full of Thy riches." Psalm 104:24.

Who tells the scarlet runner bean always to turn to the right as it climbs, and the honeysuckle and the hop always to turn to the left?

Who tells the birds how to travel back from distant continents across strange lands and unknown seas to their old haunts? Who tells the salmon how to find the mouth of the river, even the very pool where they were born? Who tells the baby turtle, newly hatched and far inland, how to find its way to the sea?

How is an apple made? Who planned a core in every one? Who put the seeds inside the grape, and gave to every fruit the power to make a tree like the one that bore it?

It is God, Creator of heaven and earth, and He alone. "Great and marvellous are Thy works, Lord God Almighty; just and true are Thy ways, Thou King of saints." Revelation 15:3.

And all this tells us that God does care for little things. He is not so absorbed in moving the stars through space that He has no thought of us. Every "speck of dust" on the "golf ball" is precious to Him. He loves little children best of all, and He wants them to love Him, too.

And if they do, what a surprise He has in store for them! He tells us that "eye hath not seen, nor ear heard, neither have entered into the heart of man, the things which God hath prepared for them that love Him." 1 Corinthians 2:9.

And when God starts planning surprises, we may well expect something beyond our brightest dreams. Think of it! The hand that made the stars is preparing our heavenly home! The fingers that fashioned the fairest flowers of earth are filling that home with riches untold. It will be like the lovely garden of Eden before Adam and Eve sinned and brought God's curse upon it.

So the wonders of the world we know today are as nothing compared with the wonders of the world we shall know tomorrow. And that is why we should all be glad that Jesus is coming soon. For when He who lived and died for us in the long ago returns, He will take all who love Him to His Father's gloryland. There He will reveal His choicest treasures and tell us all the secrets He has kept from us so long. Everybody will be supremely happy. "God shall wipe

PAINTING BY HARRY ANDERSON

The wonders of the world we know do not compare with the wonders of heaven.

away all tears from their eyes; and there shall be no more death, neither sorrow, nor crying, neither shall there be any more pain." Revelation 21:4. "And they shall see His face." Revelation 22:4.

We surely must plan to be there, children, and the day draws near when this lovely promise will come true.

Poor Priscilla

"Oh dear!" cried Barbara, wringing her hands, "what can be the matter with Priscilla? I must get the doctor at once."

So, laying poor Priscilla down on her pretty white bed, Barbara went over to the electric light switch and pretended that it was the telephone.

"Hello! Is that you, Dr. Pills?"

"Yes, madam," came a voice from the other side of the door. "This is Dr. Pills. What can I do for you?"

"Oh, Doctor, my poor Priscilla has been taken so ill. Please do come at once."

"I will come at once," said the voice in the corridor. "My car is waiting at the gate, so I shall only be a few moments."

Barbara returned to Priscilla's bedside, and tried hard to weep some tears over her. There was a knock at the door, and she opened it.

"Ah, so here you are, Dr. Pills. I'm so glad you've come."

Dr. Pills, wearing Father's best hat and carrying his brief case, walked over to the bed. He tried to look very serious as he took off his gloves.

"Let me feel her pulse," he said, taking Priscilla's tiny hand.

"Ah, very fast, very fast," he murmured.

"Poor Priscilla!" said Barbara.

"Now let me look at her tongue," said Dr. Pills.

"I'm afraid she's too ill to open her mouth," said Barbara. "Do tell me what you think is the matter."

"A very serious case," said Dr. Pills. "Very serious."

"Oh, what shall I do, what shall I do?" cried Barbara, wringing her hands.

"Do?" said Dr. Pills. "There is only one thing to do. You must treat the child better. You have been feeding her wrong. She has acute indigestion, and will probably die."

"Die, oh dear! How terrible!" exclaimed Barbara. "What should I feed her on to make her well and strong again?"

"Ahem!" said Dr. Pills. "Let me see. This child has been eating too much candy. She has been eating it all day long and it has ruined her stomach. You must stop giving her candy, except at meals."

"But she will cry so!" said Barbara.

"Never mind," said Dr. Pills. "Better cry than die. Children must not eat between meals. It is very bad for them. And, let me see, does she eat plenty of greens?"

"Oh, no, Doctor. She hates greens. Whenever I bring them on the table, she grumbles terribly."

"Never mind," said Dr. Pills sternly. "Better grumble than be ill. She must eat some greens every day—lettuce, cabbage, sprouts, cauliflower, and things like that."

"Not all of them every day!"

"Oh dear no!" said Dr. Pills. "But one of them at least every day. And let me see, does the child get enough fruit?"

"She likes bananas and pears, but they are so expensive I can't afford to give her very many."

"She must have plenty of fruit. Stop giving her sugary cakes and pastries, and give her apples and oranges instead."

"I once heard," said Barbara, "that an apple a day keeps the doctor away. Is there any truth in it?"

"Certainly," said Dr. Pills. "I shall *never* have to come back again if you do that—unless, of course, she catches measles or scarlet fever."

"Oh, thank you so much, Dr. Pills," said Barbara. "How much is your fee?"

"My fee?" said Dr. Pills. "My fee is two dollars and a half."

"Rather high, isn't it?" said Barbara, taking two big buttons and five little buttons out of her purse.

"My usual charge," said Dr. Pills. "Thank you. I trust your daughter will soon be better. And mind you follow my instructions."

"I will," said Barbara as she closed the door. "But Peter," she called, "you won't forget to put Father's hat back in the proper place, will you?"

Disappearing Donald

A strange thing about Donald was the way he would disappear sometimes, usually just when Mamma wanted him for some important errand.

"Donald, Donald!" Mamma would call, but no Donald would come.

Sometimes she would call for him all over the house, then from the bedroom window, perhaps, then from the back door, then from the front door, and still there would be no sign of Donald.

Then, just when she would be getting really anxious, Donald would silently slip into the room where Mamma was working just as if nothing had happened.

Then when Mamma would say, "Donald, why didn't you

come when I called you?" he would say, "I'm sorry, Mamma, but I came as quickly as I could."

But when Mamma asked, "Donald, where have you been all this time?" all he would say was, "Aaaaaah, that's a secret!"

And no matter how Mamma might coax to find out, she never got any farther than that long, mysterious "Aaaaaah!"

One day, when Mamma wasn't feeling any too well, Donald disappeared again.

"Oh dear," she said to herself, "where does the boy go? And why does he run away like this? I wish he wouldn't bother me so when I'm feeling tired."

At last Donald reappeared.

"Donald," she said, "now this must stop. I wanted you to help me with the dishes, and you're just making my headache worse and worse."

"Oh, I'm so sorry," said Donald. "Where's the towel? I'll wipe the dishes now. Really, I will, Mamma."

They worked together for a while, Donald with a faraway look on his face most of the time.

Presently he said, "Mamma, did you say you've got a headache?"

"Yes, dear."

"Is it very, very bad?"

"Yes, very bad."

"Ah," said Donald, relapsing into silence.

No sooner was the last dish wiped than Donald vanished once more, slipping so silently out of the kitchen that Mamma did not notice his going.

"Donald," she called presently, but there was no Donald.

"So he's gone again!" she exclaimed. "But he can't be far away. I'll find him this time."

She felt he could not have gone out into the yard, or she would have heard the door shut. He must be in the house somewhere.

Mamma went into the dining room and looked under the table, behind the piano and the curtains, but there was no Donald to be found. She did the same in the living room, with the same result. Then she went upstairs and started on the bedrooms, opening all the cupboards and looking behind the doors.

In Donald's room there was only a table and one small bed; so she didn't spend much time there. But as she turned to leave, she heard a slight rustling noise under the bed, and then Donald's head poked out.

"Donald!" exclaimed Mamma. "So there you are!"

"Mamma," asked Donald, with a serious look on his little face, "are you feeling better? I mean, is your headache better?"

"Well," said Mamma, hesitating, "I think it is. But why do you ask?"

"Oh, Mamma," said Donald solemnly, "I've been under the bed asking Jesus to make you better."

Mamma's headache got better quicker that day than it ever had before. At last she had found out where Donald went when he disappeared.

God's Lifeboatmen

Here and there along the coasts of various countries are to be found the lifeboat stations. If you live at the seaside, of course you know about lifeboats. If you don't, still you must have read about them many times, and

maybe you have looked admiringly at brightly painted lifeboats when on your vacation.

But lifeboats are not merely seaside ornaments. They are made to be used, and the reason why so few of us see them in use is that they only put to sea —except for practice—in times of storm and peril, often in the dead of night, when most little boys and girls are fast asleep in bed.

I have never seen a lifeboat launched in a winter blizzard, but what a great thrill that would be! To watch the brave lifeboatmen, gathered at the call to service from their cozy firesides, perhaps from their warm beds, donning their life belts and taking their places in the boat; to hear the word of command to let go, to see the boat with its precious human freight gliding down the slipway and plunging amid clouds of spray into the storm-swept sea—I would stay up any night to see such a sight as that, wouldn't you?

From the time the first lifeboat was launched in 1786 at Bamborough, England, tens of thousands of lives have been saved from untimely death by the gallant men of the lifeboat service.

Yet, though so many lives have been saved, it has not been without sacrifice. Time and again lifeboats have capsized in the rough seas, and their brave crews have been drowned. Even nowadays, when lifeboats are made so that they cannot sink, and so that they will right themselves if capsized, the men who

man them always carry their lives in their hands when they put out to a wreck, for there's no knowing when a stormy sea will smash their boats on hidden rocks.

There are indeed no men more worthy of our respect and honor than the gallant crews of our lifeboats, and on dark winter nights, when the wind is howling around our houses, we may well remember them in our prayers.

Still there are other lifeboatmen besides those who venture their lives on the sea.

Life is somewhat like the sea, isn't it? And all the people of the world are the ships floating upon it. There are big ships and little ships, steamers and sailing boats, and tiny little row-boats. Some are sailing proudly across the waters, others are battling with the winds of trouble, still others have sprung leaks through the stress of the journey, while many that have struck hidden rocks are sinking beneath the waves.

All around us there is great need of lifeboatmen today. What can be done? What can you do? There's your little boat —can't you turn it into a lifeboat and help somebody in need?

Many greathearted men and women have had this same beautiful thought in times gone by. You have probably heard of some of them. There was George Mueller, for instance, whose heart was touched with compassion for all the poor little children left alone on the great sea of life when their fathers and mothers died. Seeing their need, he made of himself a lifeboatman, and set out to rescue them. In this he was wonderfully blessed of God, and during the first hundred years after he opened his famous orphan homes in Bristol, over 20,000 poor little orphans found a refuge there. During that time, too, and solely in answer to prayer, over $15,000,000 flowed in to pay the expenses. Surely George Mueller was one of God's own lifeboatmen.

Then there was Dr. Barnardo. When but a young medical student, he saw eleven poor little London waifs asleep in a gutter under an open sky. To him they were like little boats sinking in the sea of life. He made up his mind to do what he could to rescue them, and started what has become known everywhere as Dr. Barnardo's Homes. That was many years ago. Since then over 120,000 boys and girls have been admitted, fed, clothed, and trained. "No Destitute Child Ever Refused Admission" was the motto the goldenhearted doctor set up over his doors, and never since has it been forgotten. In normal

times, about five children are added daily. There is a constant family of 8,400. What a wonderful lifesaving work! Surely Dr. Barnardo and all his self-sacrificing helpers belong also to the noble order of God's lifeboatmen.

Of course you have heard, too, of William Booth, who started the Salvation Army. When but a lad he saw some children crying in the streets for bread. These little storm-tossed souls, he thought, needed someone to rescue them. So he, too, became a lifeboatman. He began to preach in the open air, and he sent his converts out to help the poor, the hungry, the outcast, and the prisoners. Gradually his work grew until thousands were following his lead in trying to help those in need.

In one year the Salvation Army now supplies hungry people with more than twenty million meals.

And besides all this it cares for thousands of poor mothers and needy children, and unemployed men, and those who have been in prison and want to start life over again.

What a marvelous record of rescue belongs to the lifeboats

of General William Booth and his many faithful friends!

Maybe you've heard, too, of a man called Prebendary Carlile. As a young man he felt God was calling him to be one of His lifeboatmen, and so, with a group of Christian workers, he went into a London slum to begin work. But in this case the people did not want to be rescued, and showers of cabbage stumps and rotten fruit greeted these brave, kindly souls. As time passed, however, the situation changed, and many lived to bless the ministry of the splendid workers of the Church Army, which they founded.

In one year this organization of God's lifeboatmen provided over 600,000 beds in clean lodging homes for poor men and lads, and over 120,000 for women and girls. More than 100,000 visits have been paid to prisoners in their cells, and much other Christian work has been done. Who can tell how many little boats have been saved from sinking by this beautiful labor of mercy and love?

Then there was William Wilberforce, who, over one hundred and fifty years ago, championed the cause of the slaves. He looked out upon these poor, downtrodden, mistreated people as a lifeboatman looks out upon a wreck at sea. And they were

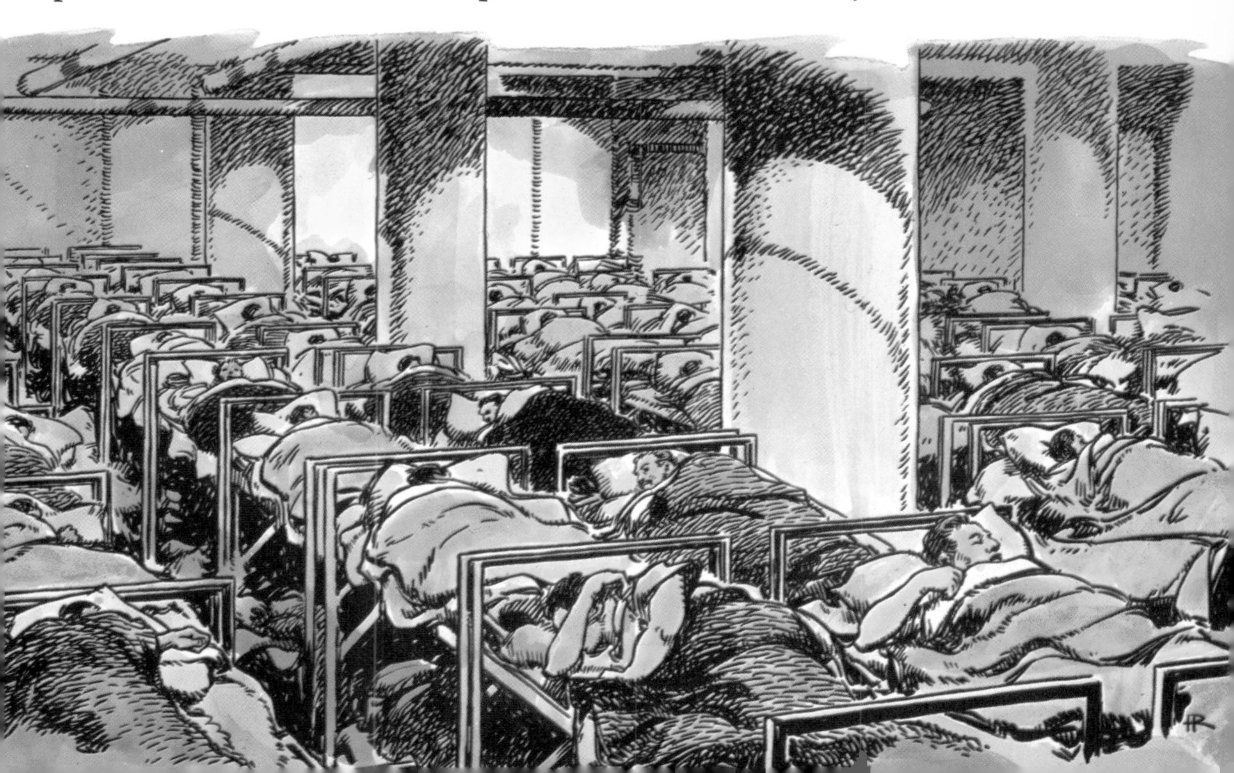

sad wrecks, too. Bullied and beaten and starved, torn from their homes and friends, and worked well-nigh to death, their little boats were indeed sinking. How they needed someone to come to their rescue! Wilberforce heard their cry and answered it, devoting his life to the cause of procuring their freedom throughout the British Empire.

Abraham Lincoln, another of God's lifeboatmen, won freedom for all slaves in North America.

There was David Livingstone, too, who gave his life for Africa. He was yet another of the great men who helped to abolish slavery. When he saw the terrible way the Arab slave traders were treating the poor natives, he determined that he would do all he could to bring this horrible system to an end. He became, as well, the leader of a great army of missionaries who have since gone out to that dark land to tell the people there the beautiful story of the love of Jesus for them.

To every land God's lifeboatmen have sailed to help in various ways in this glorious work of rescue, not only to Africa, but to India, China, South America, and the far-off Pacific Islands. Everywhere around the great wide world they have gone, and still are going, bringing a message of love and hope and salvation to thousands whose little ships would otherwise sink in darkness and despair.

Wouldn't you like to be a lifeboatman, too? You may never be able to wear a cork life belt and ride gallantly out over the stormy sea to some steamer in distress, but you can help in the work of rescue just the same. There are many wrecks on the sea of life, not far away from you, and many little boats may sink if you do not help them. You may not be a Wilberforce or a Livingstone or a Barnardo or a Lincoln, but that is no reason why you should not do what you can just where you are, and who knows what God will make of you when you grow up?

You may feel very small now, and think that you cannot help at all, but it is surprising how much blessing even a little child can bring into people's lives. Do you know, there's nothing so cheering, nothing that so makes worried folks forget their troubles, as the smile of a little child? The gentle words of sympathy, the offer of hands and feet in willing service that only a child can make, can sometimes do more to brighten sad and weary hearts than—well—than dozens of bottles of medicine from the Doctor. You try them on Mother when she's very tired, or on Daddy when he seems a bit "blue," or on your little friends at school when they're out of sorts.

Oh, yes, you don't have to wait until you're grown up to become one of God's lifeboatmen. You can be one today. Why not decide to join the ranks now?

Hurrah for the Baby!

Hurrah for the—— But sh-h! Don't say it too loud, or he might wake up, and then I'd never get these stories done.

You see, he's just the biggest time-consumer that ever came into our house. Even when he's asleep he's so beautiful that I could stand and stare at him by the hour. And when he's awake, well, those great blue eyes that look up at mine keep me glued by his little bed. Wonderful eyes they are, that seem so full of understanding, as though behind them in that tiny head were stored the wisdom of the ages. But there, if you have a baby in your house, you will understand.

And when he smiles—well, it's the hardest job I have to drag myself away. I could stay and watch his happy little face and listen to his cooings and gurglings and bubblings forever and ever. At least I think I could, if they would last that long. For surely a baby's laugh is the most heavenly music ever heard on earth.

Really, I don't know how some folks get along without a

OLOR PHOTO BY SHOSTAL

ely a baby's laugh is the most heavenly music ever heard on earth.

baby. They don't know what they're missing, do they? And though we've had this one only a very little while, he's been the uncrowned king of the house the whole time. Everybody walks on tiptoe when he's going to sleep. Everybody rushes to pick him up when he wakes. Everybody scrambles to push his baby buggy when it's time for him to go for a ride. Everybody wants to kiss away his tears when he cries. He has six lords and ladies in waiting ready to execute his slightest behest, and what more could any monarch desire? Nothing is too good for him, and there's nothing that anybody will not give up for him. How true it is that there's nothing that brings so much love into a home as a baby!

Of course, we thought once that he was going to be a little girl, and we had heaps of little girls' names ready for him. But you couldn't give a little boy a lot of girls' names, could you? Just think what he would have to put up with at school! So we had to start all over again. Don't tell anybody, will you, but I searched in vain through a thousand pages of *Who's Who* to find one that would be good enough for him, and then found one in a volume of *Bedtime Stories!*

But, girl or boy, what did it matter anyway? He's a baby —one of the loveliest gifts God ever gives to man.

What fun we have had with him from the very day he came to town! How we have watched the dear, dainty, wee bundle of life gradually unfolding like one of those amazing Oriental flowers you drop into a glass of water! What joy to feel his tiny fingers clutching ours with ever-increasing strength, to see him staring wonderingly at his own bewitching little toes!

Oh, yes, he can cry, too, when he is hungry or uncomfortable, loud enough to wake the whole neighborhood; but then that's all part of the great, glorious game of having a baby.

Wouldn't you like to have one, too? I'm sure you would, but you couldn't buy ours for—well—for all the money in your money box. You ask his big sister and all his brothers, and just hear what they would say.

Yes! Hurrah for the baby! It's all right now, for he's wide awake. How happy he looks after his nap.

How Bobby's Prayers Were Answered

Bobby was just old enough to have an erector set of his own. He had been given one for his birthday a few weeks before, and was now struggling to make up one of the patterns in the book. It was a rather difficult task for him, for his chubby fingers were so small they couldn't pick up the screws easily; but he was working away with much patience and determination.

While Bobby and his erector set were sprawled out all over the dining room table, Mamma was in the kitchen washing up the dishes after supper.

After a while she heard someone talking in the other room, and as she knew no one else was in the house except Bobby, she stopped her work to listen.

"There's nuffin' in it; there's nuffin' in it," she heard a little voice say. "I knew there was nuffin' in it."

Mamma left the sink and peeped through the crack of the dining room door. To her astonishment she saw Bobby just getting up off his knees, and heard him saying again to himself, "There's nuffin' in it."

Wondering what he meant, she went into the dining room.
"Nothing in what?" she asked.

"In prayer," said Bobby solemnly.

"Bobby dear!" exclaimed Mamma, "what do you mean?"

"I asked God to help me make this thing go right, and He hasn't done it," said Bobby.

Mamma would have liked to smile, but she dared not. This was too serious a matter.

"Well, darling," she said, "sometimes God doesn't answer prayers immediately. Some people have to wait a long time for their prayers to be answered, but He always answers them sometime, somehow."

Bobby grunted as though he did not agree with this explanation of the ways of God.

"Perhaps, darling," said Mamma, "you have done enough for tonight. Why not leave it till morning, and go to bed now? Maybe it will be easier then for you."

Bobby, who was really very tired, thought this was not such a bad idea, and putting all the pieces back into the box, he went upstairs to bed.

He said his prayers as usual, and although he had announced so definitely that there was "nuffin' in it," he asked God once more to help him fix his erector in the morning.

When he had gone to sleep, Mamma had a happy thought. She had never worked with an erector set in her life, but she got it out and started to carry on with the job Bobby had begun. Never had her fingers felt so clumsy as when she tried to get the little nuts to fit on the bolts, and more than once she hurt her fingers with the screw driver. Slowly but surely, however, the pieces went together. Mamma began to get really interested, and to wonder why she had not become an engineer instead of a Mother.

At last the toy was finished, and with pride and great care Mamma carried it upstairs and placed it where Bobby could see it just as soon as he should wake in the morning.

Morning came, and Bobby, opening his eyes, shrieked with delight.

"Mamma, Mamma!" he called at the top of his voice. "Come quickly and see what's here on my bed."

Mamma ran in, all smiles.

"Look—— Look, Mamma,"

he cried excitedly. "See, God did answer my prayer, after all."

"Yes," said Mamma, "isn't that wonderful!"

Bobby looked thoughtful for a moment.

"I wonder, Mamma," he said, "did you put this together?"

"Why—er—yes," said Mamma hesitatingly. "I did it last night after you had gone to sleep."

"Then it wasn't God after all," said Bobby, with a trace of disappointment in his voice.

"Oh, yes, it was," said Mamma, "because you see, He made me think about doing it, and He helped me such a lot, too."

"Oh," grunted Bobby, not quite sure yet.

"Anyway," said Mamma, "God has so many boys to care for that He sometimes lets their Mammas help Him answer their prayers."

The Boy With a Light

It may be hard to believe, but here's a story about a boy who came from nowhere and vanished into nowhere, and yet I shall never forget him and the kindly deed he did.

What a night that was! I was driving alone out of London when all of a sudden I found myself in the midst of a thick bank of fog.

It was so dense that I could see absolutely nothing, not a house, nor a tree, nor a white line, nor even the edge of the road. My headlights only made things worse, for the fog reflected the light and made just a blanket of fire in front of me.

For a few moments I tried to drive on, but almost immediately I felt the wheels go bump, bump! and I knew that I had run over something.

Stopping the car, I jumped out and peered around in the murky darkness, to find that all four wheels had mounted the curb!

I was thankful that I had not knocked anybody down, but now I had to get back on the road.

Very slowly I backed until I felt that bump, bump again, for I knew then that I must at least be off the sidewalk.

But now I couldn't be sure whether I was headed toward London or home. There was absolutely no way to tell; not an indication of any kind anywhere. I just had to hope for the best.

"Well," I thought, "it looks as if I'm going to be stuck out here for the rest of the night, or at least till the fog lifts, which may take hours." And it is not very pleasant, let me tell you, to be out on a main road in a fog. You never can tell when some other car is going to hit you.

At that moment a strange thing happened.

Through the window beside me peered the face of a little boy. He was holding something in his hand.

"May I help you?" he asked politely.

"Help me!" I said laughingly. "How can you help me? The fog is too bad."

"Oh, I think I can," he said. "You see, I have a light."

I looked at his "light" and laughed again. It was only a cheap little flashlight, throwing but the faintest beam.

"My big headlights don't do any good," I said; "so how can you help with yours?"

"Oh," he said, "I'll show you. I'll go ahead and shine my little light on the edge of the road, and then you can shine your big lights on my back, and we'll get along fine."

"Well," I said, "you're a bright boy anyway. I'll try it and we'll see if it works."

He went ahead with his light and I followed.

Straining my eyes as hard as I could, I found I could just pick out the form of the little chap as he walked slowly by the side of the road, shining his flashlight ahead of him.

On and on we went together. I don't know how far it was, but it may well have been more than a mile. Then suddenly the air cleared, and I knew we had left the worst of the fog bank behind.

PAINTING BY HARRY BAERG

I stopped the car and put my head out of the window to thank the dear boy and give him some reward. But he wasn't there! He had vanished! He had gone back, no doubt, to help somebody else through the fog.

I have often thought of that boy since then and wished I knew his name. If by any chance he should read this story, I hope he will write to me. For it seems to me that he is just the sort of little boy that God loves best—anxious to help others without thought of thanks or reward.

And that little light of his reminds me that God has put into the hands of each one of us the light of His word—the Holy Bible—hoping that we will shine it before others who have lost their way, and lead them gently out of the fog of sin into the brightness of truth and salvation, and the sunlight of His love.

QUADE

The Baby a Princess Found

Once upon a time there was a little baby, and his Mamma put him in a little boat down by the river, in some bulrushes. Then she asked God to send His angels to look after her baby and keep him safe from the wicked king who wanted to kill him.

The next day a pretty princess came down to the river to bathe. She saw the little boat in the bulrushes, and she said, "Oh, what a pretty little baby! I must have him for my own."

Just then a little girl ran up and said, "Please, ma'am, would you like me to get someone to look after the baby for you?"

And the pretty princess said, "Please do."

So the little girl ran as fast as her legs would carry her all the way home, and she cried out, "Mamma, come quick! The princess has found baby brother!"

Mamma dropped what

AINTING BY LESTER QUADE

, what a pretty little baby! I must have him for my own," the princess said.

she was doing, and ran, just as she was, all the way down to the river. There she saw the pretty princess and the other ladies and the bulrushes and the little boat and her darling baby.

Then the pretty princess said to the Mamma, "Will you look after this baby for me, please?"

And the Mamma said, "Indeed, I will." And she hugged her little baby ever so tight and ran back home with him and the little girl as fast as ever they could go. And they all lived happily for a long time afterward.

Can you guess the baby's name?

Yes, it was Moses, who grew up to be a great leader of God's people.

New Clothes for Old

When you see a flock of sheep feeding peacefully in a field, you probably say, "Oh, Mamma, look at the pretty sheep!" Not for a moment do you think of all the trouble the shepherds have taken to tend those sheep through the cold winter.

If the lambs are born early in the year, before the snow has melted, many of them die of the cold. Sometimes the mother sheep dies as well. The shepherd is sad about this, as you can imagine.

Sometimes it happens that a mother sheep will die and leave a baby lamb. The shepherd does not want to lose the lamb as well, but what can he do? No other sheep will take the lamb

Russ Harlan

and look after it. They are not like human beings, for they will only look after their own little ones.

So what do you suppose the shepherd does? Well, he looks over his flock, and finds a mother sheep who has just lost her lamb. He takes the poor dead lamb, removes its skin, and places it carefully over the body of the live lamb that has lost its mother. You can see the shepherd doing this in our picture. It is just like putting on an overcoat, isn't it? Anyhow, the shepherd takes the poor little orphan lamb over to the mother sheep that has just lost her own baby. She smells the lamb all over, decides that it must surely be her own, and takes it to herself.

This gives us a beautiful illustration of what the love of Jesus does for us. Many times you must have heard the minister say in church that Jesus "covers us with the robe of His righteousness." Perhaps you have wondered just what he meant.

Now you can understand it easily, can't you? We are like the poor little orphan lamb. If we love Jesus, the slain Lamb, His goodness is wrapped, like a cloak, around us, and His Father accepts us, not because we are worthy of His love, but because He sees around us the glorious goodness of His own Son, and God welcomes us as His own dear children.

That doesn't mean, of course, that we can do what we like afterward. God truly accepts us because of what Jesus has done for us, but we must ever try by His grace to live to please Him. We must not be content just to look like Jesus outside. God wants us to be like Jesus through and through.

And that is where we differ from the poor little orphan lamb. He wears his covering only a few days until his mother gets used to him. We, however, must wear the righteousness of Jesus always, daily growing in grace and beauty of character.

PAINTING BY RUSSELL HARLAN

us wraps His goodness around us like a cloak and we are then accepted by the Father.

Faithful Unto Death

As Edith came in from school, Mother saw at once that something was wrong.

"What is the matter, dear?" she asked. "You look as if all the troubles in the world were on your shoulders."

"Oh, dear!" cried Edith, "I'm tired of their teasing me, day in, and day out. It's always the same."

"What do they say to you?" asked Mother. "You mustn't mind a little teasing. Every little girl gets teased at school some time or other."

"Oh, it isn't just ordinary teasing," said Edith. "It's the way they keep calling me names, just because I keep the Sabbath. Why can't they leave me alone?"

Mother sat down and drew Edith upon her lap.

"Let me tell you a story," she said, "then you will feel much happier about it. It's about three boys who were taken away into a foreign country and made to live with people who didn't believe as they did. It was very hard for them. They wanted to remain loyal to God and His laws, but everyone around them was a heathen and a worshiper of idols. If they ever dared to speak of their religion, the people of the land would laugh at them. Because they tried to be good, the people would do all they could to annoy them and find fault.

"Then one day they were brought to a very severe test. The king of that country took it into his head to make a great idol. It was a very large one, all of pure gold. He was very proud of it, and determined that everyone in his kingdom should bow down to it. So he issued a decree that on a certain day all the people should gather on a great plain around the idol, and at a given signal fall down on their faces before it. To make sure that everyone would obey him, he threatened that if any should fail to bow down to it, he would have them cast into a red-hot furnace.

"The three boys realized that the biggest test of their lives had come. They could not avoid it, for everybody was sent out on the plain. Not a soul was allowed to remain behind in the city. So there they found themselves, in the midst of a vast concourse of people, facing the great golden image that stood in the center of the crowd. How their hearts must have beat as they waited for the signal to be given! People who knew them whispered together, wondering what they would do now.

HEASLIP

"At last the king's band began to play. There was a great shout, and the tens of thousands of people threw themselves prostrate upon the ground. Over all that vast plain only three figures remained erect. They could not have been more conspicuous. People began to look up at them out of the corners of their eyes. The news spread rapidly from end to end of the multitude. 'The three Hebrew boys have refused to bow down to the king's image.' What excitement!

"There must have been a tremendous stir. Everybody knew what the penalty was, and they waited to see what the king would do. Meanwhile the three boys stood there, their faces pale and set, bravely awaiting their fate.

"The king sent for them. He was in a bad temper. He asked

PAINTING BY WILLIAM HEASLIP

them what they meant by disobeying his decree, and warned them again of the fiery furnace. Respectfully, but firmly, the boys replied, 'Our God whom we serve is able to deliver us from the burning fiery furnace, and He will deliver us out of thine hand, O king. But if not, be it known unto thee, O king, that we will not serve thy gods, nor worship the golden image which thou hast set up.'

"At this the king was still more furious, and told his soldiers to heat the furnace seven times hotter than usual. Then the three boys were bound and cast into it. That must have been a terrible moment for them. But they did not waver, not even when they felt the fierce heat of the fire upon them.

"Then a wonderful thing happened. The fire burned their bonds, but left them untouched. Suddenly Jesus Himself appeared among them and walked with them in the midst of the fire. The king saw the four figures walking there, and was terrified. He called to the boys to come out of the furnace, and triumphantly they strode forth. The Bible says that not 'an hair of their heads was singed, neither were their coats changed, nor the smell of fire had passed on them.'

"The whole concourse of people witnessed the miracle and must have been greatly impressed. As for the king, he admitted that the God whom the boys served was greater than his image. 'There is no other god that can deliver after this sort,' he said. And so, because those boys were faithful, and were not afraid to suffer even death for what they believed, the whole nation was blessed, and even the king was led to see the folly of his idolatry."

"I think I can see what you mean," said Edith.

"I'm sure you can," said Mother. "You are God's little wit-

ness to His truth at your school. You must be loyal to Him at all costs. You know that the Sabbath is right and that God in His Word commands us to keep the seventh day holy. The others may tease you about it, but that doesn't matter. If you are loyal to Him in spite of all the unkind things they say and do, why, Jesus will walk with you at school as He did with the boys in the fiery furnace long ago."

"I think I feel better about it now," said Edith. "I'll try to be as brave as those three boys."

The Man Who Always Said His Prayers

John and his mother were in a city restaurant. It was packed with people, and they were waiting more or less patiently to be served. At last the waitress appeared, bringing them their dinner.

John, who was very hungry, seized his knife and fork, and prepared to eat. Then he hesitated.

Mother had bowed her head to say grace. John looked at her, then at the people all around, and blushing just a little, took his first bite.

"You didn't forget something, did you?" asked Mother, as she started to eat.

"No," said John, "but everybody was looking at me."

"But what does that matter?" asked Mother. "If it is right to thank God for our food at home, surely we should do it everywhere we go."

"But the people stare so," said John. "It makes me feel so uncomfortable."

"It shouldn't," said Mother. "We should never be afraid of people when we are doing right."

John went on eating vigorously, and in silence. The matter was apparently forgotten.

But when John asked for a story that night, Mother had one ready for him. Indeed, John was surprised how quickly Mother thought of one this time, for sometimes she took a long time to do so.

"This is the story," said Mother, "of the man who always said his prayers."

"What, prayed all day long?" asked John.

"Oh, no," said Mother, "but he always said his prayers, no matter what people said of him or how they treated him. His name was Daniel, and it was his practice to pray three times a day, once in the morning when he got up, once at dinnertime, and once just before he went to bed."

"That's once more than we do," said John.

"Yes," said Mother, "and that is perhaps why he was such a good man. Anyhow, that was his habit. Now, in those days people did not live in houses like ours. There was no glass in their windows, and unless the curtains were drawn, people could readily see in. So it often happened that passers-by saw Daniel praying in his room. They did not disturb him, but they peered in, wondering, perhaps, just what he was doing.

"One day some of his enemies happened to pass the window, and seeing Daniel at prayer, thought of a new way of causing him harm. Having much influence with the king, they went to him with a decree they had written out and asked him to sign it. They said, 'We want you to make a law that if anyone asks a petition of any god or man other than yourself during the next month, he shall be cast to the lions.' Of course it was a very foolish decree, but the king, feeling flattered at the idea, signed it, and it became law.

"At once the law was published all over the kingdom, and people began to wonder how it would work out. Many knew about Daniel's habit of saying his prayers three times a day, and they said to one another, 'I wonder what he will do now?'

"Early the next morning people began to gather round Daniel's house. 'Will he pray at his window, as usual?' was the question on everybody's lips.

"More and more people came. Every eye was fixed on Daniel's window.

"At last the hour of prayer arrived. Daniel knelt in his usual place and prayed as he had always done. He made no attempt to draw the curtains and hide himself, though he could easily have done so."

"Did he know about the law?" asked John.

"Oh, yes," said Mother, "he must have known. He was the chief ruler of the land, next to the king, and his servants would surely have brought him word about what his enemies had persuaded the king to do in his absence. That is why what he did was so brave. He realized what he might have to suffer for saying his prayers, but he said them just the same.

"How the people must have stared in astonishment and disbelief as they saw him kneeling there! I'm sure some said,

'Brave man!' and others, 'How dare he disobey the king?'

"His enemies were there, too, and they at once ran off to tell the king. They were overjoyed that Daniel had so soon fallen into the trap they had laid for him.

" 'Do you know,' they said to the king, 'that fellow Daniel has actually dared to defy your decree already? He is saying his prayers as usual now. You must have him arrested and cast to the lions at once.'

"Now, the king thought a great deal of Daniel. He knew that Daniel was a good man, and he valued his wise counsel in caring for his kingdom. The last thing he wanted was to see Daniel cast to the lions. He felt so sorry that his foolish pride had led him to sign the decree. If only he had thought about it more, he would have realized that his faithful minister would be affected by it. Now, however, he could do nothing. Try as he would, he could find no way out. Having signed the decree, he had to abide by it. So at last, very reluctantly, he gave orders that Daniel should be cast to the lions.

"The soldiers went round to Daniel's house and carried him off. Dense crowds of people watched him being taken away, and followed him to the den of lions. They saw the gates opened and the poor man thrown in. Most of them expected that he would be killed in a moment, but a great surprise awaited them.

"Even in the den of lions, with the great beasts pacing up and down around him, Daniel prayed to God. And God heard and answered him.

"All that night the king could not sleep, and very early in the morning he went alone to the den of lions and cried sorrowfully, 'O Daniel, servant of the living God, is thy God,

PAINTING BY HARRY BAERG

d sent His angel to protect Daniel from the hungry lions, and they did not touch him.

whom thou servest continually, able to deliver thee from the lions?'

"Then to his great joy the king heard a familiar voice coming from the den, and Daniel said, 'My God hath sent His angel, and hath shut the lions' mouths, that they have not hurt me.'

"At this the king was ever so glad, and at once commanded that Daniel should be taken out of the pit and his enemies thrown in. After that he made another decree, which he sent out to every part of his kingdom, telling of the power of the great God whom Daniel served and worshiped. 'I make a decree,' he wrote, 'That in every dominion of my kingdom men tremble and fear before the God of Daniel: for He is the living God, and stedfast for ever, and His kingdom that which shall not be destroyed, and His dominion shall be even unto the end. He delivereth and rescueth, and He worketh signs and wonders in heaven and in earth, who hath delivered Daniel from the power of the lions.'

"And so," concluded Mother, "because Daniel was faithful in saying his prayers every day, no matter who was looking at him, or what he might have to suffer for it, this beautiful testimony of the king to the power of Daniel's God was sent out to all the people of the world. Who can tell how much good it accomplished?"

John was silent for a little while.

"I wish I had said my grace at dinnertime today, Mother," he said presently. "I think Daniel would have done it."

"You must remember it next time," said Mother.

And you may be sure that he did.

A Page of Blessings

When Jesus lived on the earth, before He would eat bread He first blessed it.

You remember He looked up to heaven and blessed the bread before He fed the five thousand hungry people on the mountainside. And from this example of the Master has come down to us the beautiful custom of "saying grace" before meals.

I wonder what you say when you "ask the blessing" or "say grace." I know one little boy who used to say, very simply, and with his eyes tight shut: "Thank God for this good food. Amen."

That's very brief, isn't it? But God hears every prayer.

When I was in Birmingham, England, once, I heard a little girl say this blessing, and I thought it was very beautiful indeed:

"Thank You for the world so sweet,
Thank You for the food we eat,
Thank You for the birds that sing,
Thank You, God, for ev'rything."

One that children often say is this:

"For what we are about to receive may the Lord make us truly thankful. Amen."

You may have said that very often, but if you think a little more what the words mean, perhaps you won't say it so fast as you have done.

Here is another beautiful little blessing:

"Bless this food which now we take
And make us good for Jesus' sake. Amen."

And here is yet another:

"Dear Jesus, as our heads we bow,
For this good food we thank Thee now. Amen."

And if you do not wish to say your blessing in poetry, you can say this:

"We thank Thee, dear Lord, for this good food. Bless us now. Make us strong for Thy service. Remember the poor and needy. For Jesus' sake. Amen."

And now you won't forget to say your blessing next mealtime, will you?

Beautiful Things

How we all love to look at beautiful things—and to possess them. Beautiful girls and beautiful boys, beautiful babes and beautiful toys!

Beautiful dogs and beautiful cats.

Beautiful horses and beautiful automobiles.

Beautiful homes and beautiful gardens.

Beautiful flowers and trees and rivers and lakes—all the lovely things of nature.

Little girls like pretty dresses and lovely dolls.

Little boys like bright red cars and smart-looking locomotives.

But have you ever noticed that some things are not always so nice inside as they are outside? There is a very old saying, "All is not gold that glitters," and it is very true.

Once upon a time a Daddy I know gave his little son a fine-looking steam engine for Christmas, and the very first time the boy wound it up the spring broke. It looked good outside, but it was bad inside. Wasn't the poor little boy disappointed!

And one time a Mamma gave a little girl a most beautiful-looking doll. She was so pleased. But what do you suppose happened? Why, just as the little girl was hugging the doll and kissing its pretty face, its eyes fell in! And then it looked so ugly that the little girl felt she could never love it any more.

If you notice, you will find that many things that look very nice outside are poor and cheap and worthless inside.

Sometimes it happens this way with little boys and girls. Perhaps Mamma will dress her children in nice new clothes so that they look so clean and spotless that people think they are almost little angels from heaven. But all of a sudden something goes wrong. They begin to quarrel, and there is such a noise and such a squabbling that they become more like monkeys or wildcats than children—let alone angels!

It isn't just clothes and "looks" that make people beautiful. There are lots of little girls with the most lovely curly hair who can be as cross as bears when they can't have their own way.

And there's many a little boy looking very smart in a new

suit of clothes who can be as stubborn as a mule when he chooses.

Have you ever read the story of David? Well, when God was looking for someone to make king of Israel, many fine-looking young men presented themselves. They were tall and strong, and some of them, perhaps, well dressed. But God was not satisfied. He told His prophet Samuel to send for the brave, honest little shepherd boy who was out in the fields keeping his father's sheep. He had a beautiful face, so the Bible tells us, and he was beautiful inside too, for he had a good heart.

And God said to Samuel, "Arise, anoint him: for this is he." "For the Lord seeth not as man seeth, for man looketh on the outward appearance, but the Lord looketh on the heart." 1 Samuel 16:12, 7.

So David was made king because he was good inside as well as outside.

It is goodness, not fine clothes, that makes people beautiful. The plainest-looking folks are often the most loved because of their good hearts.

It is goodness, not outward beauty, that God looks for first. We cannot hide our crossness from God by putting on our Sabbath clothes. Nor will a kind heart pass His notice because it is clothed in rags.

And when Jesus comes back to this earth again—and He *is* coming very soon—to take His children to the wonderful home He is preparing for them, He will not bother much about their looks, you may be sure. What He will ask is, Does this child love Me? Is he a good boy? Has this little girl a loving heart?

If boys and girls do not love Him, He will just leave them behind. He simply couldn't take them into His beautiful kingdom and let them spoil it for everybody else. That is why the Bible says that when Jesus comes again, "the Son of man shall send forth His angels, and they shall gather out of His kingdom all things that offend, and them which do iniquity; and shall cast them into a furnace of fire." Matthew 13:41, 42.

We don't like to read about that; it doesn't sound nice. But then, we do not need to have that happen to us. Jesus wants us all to live with Him in His beautiful home, and He has done everything to make this possible. All He asks is that we love Him and try to be as good as He was when He was a little child. Then when He comes we shall hear Him say to us:

"'Come, you whom My Father has blessed, come into your inheritance in the realm prepared for you from the foundation of the world. For I was hungry and you fed Me, I was thirsty and you gave Me drink, I was a stranger and you entertained Me, I was unclothed and you clothed Me, I was ill and you looked after Me, I was in prison and you visited Me. . . . I tell you truly, in so far as you did it to one of these brothers of Mine, even to the least

 PAINTING BY RUSSELL HARLAN

of them, you did it to Me.'"
Matthew 25:34-40.*

This is God's idea of goodness. This is the beauty He loves. These are the beautiful things He wants us to do. Those who do them He will take to the beautiful land where all is peace and joy and happiness, and where cross and ugly things never enter.

Let's plan to be there. Let us be good today and every day and be ready when Jesus comes.

---

* From *The Bible: A New Translation* by James Moffatt. Copyright by James Moffatt, 1954. Used by permission Harper & Row, Publishers, Inc.

The Tearless Land

I suppose everybody cries sometimes. Little boys cry when they are spanked and little girls cry when they are disappointed. Even Mothers and Fathers cry now and then, I believe, when they are very, very upset.

But someday nobody will ever cry again. It seems almost too good to be true, but it is really so. There is a tearless land where everyone will be supremely happy. Sweet smiles and joyous laughter will light up their faces every moment, and nothing will dim their happiness through the eternal years.

Jesus Himself tells us about this glorious country. "In My Father's house," He says, "are many mansions. . . . I go to prepare a place for you. And if I go and prepare a place for you, I will come again, and receive you unto Myself; that where I am, there ye may be also." John 14:2, 3.

A home prepared by Jesus! Can you imagine any tears there? Can you picture anyone weeping in His presence? No indeed! Nobody cries where Jesus is. It is His supreme joy to make people happy. Where He is all tears are forgotten.

And here is another picture of that lovely land: "I saw a

at beautiful heavenly land Jesus will be with us. There will be no crying or pain.

new heaven and a new earth," writes John the apostle, "and I . . . saw the holy city, New Jerusalem, coming down from God out of heaven. . . . And God shall wipe away all tears from their eyes; and there shall be no more death, neither sorrow, nor crying, neither shall there be any more pain: for the former things are passed away." Revelation 21:1-4.

I want you to notice that it does not say that we will wipe our own tears away, or that Mother will wipe them away for us, but that God will wipe them away. Could you think of anything more beautiful? The great, the infinite, the all-powerful God, Creator of the heavens and the earth, He—He will wipe all tears away!

And once He has wiped them away, they will never flow again. In that tearless land there shall be no more sorrow, crying, pain, nor death—nothing to make us want to cry again. Forever and ever we shall feel radiantly happy. No more quarrels, no more disappointments, no more partings, no more saying good-by.

What a wonderful home it is that Jesus has prepared for us! Surely we must be ready when He comes to take us there. There is not long to wait now. Let us give our hearts to Him today.

NEWS
JOURNAL